Q&A AWESOME MAZES

Tony Tallarico

Copyright © 2008, Kidsbooks, Inc., and Tony Tallarico
www.kidsbooks.com

Printed in China

0408-1PP

Visit us at www.kidsbooks.com®

NATURE'S PRESERVATIVE

Petrified wood is the state gem of which U.S. state?

OUCH!

Start

Idaho

New Mexico

Washington

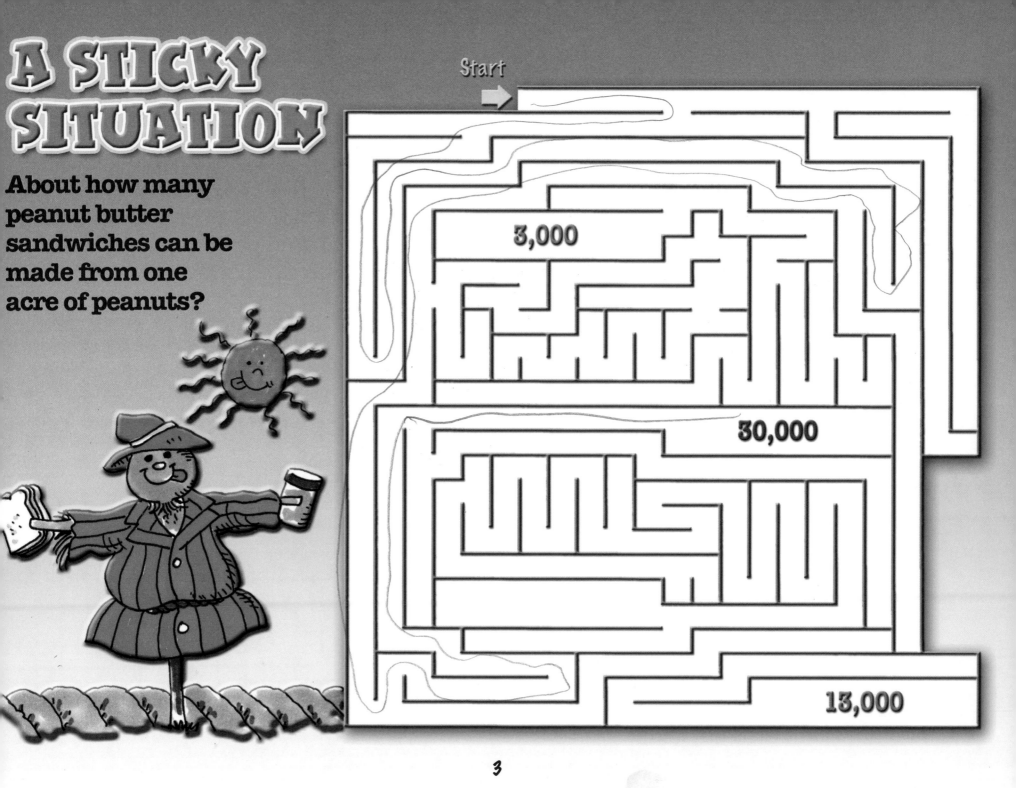

A STICKY SITUATION

About how many peanut butter sandwiches can be made from one acre of peanuts?

Start

3,000

30,000

15,000

3

CANINE CARNIVORE

An adult dog has how many teeth?

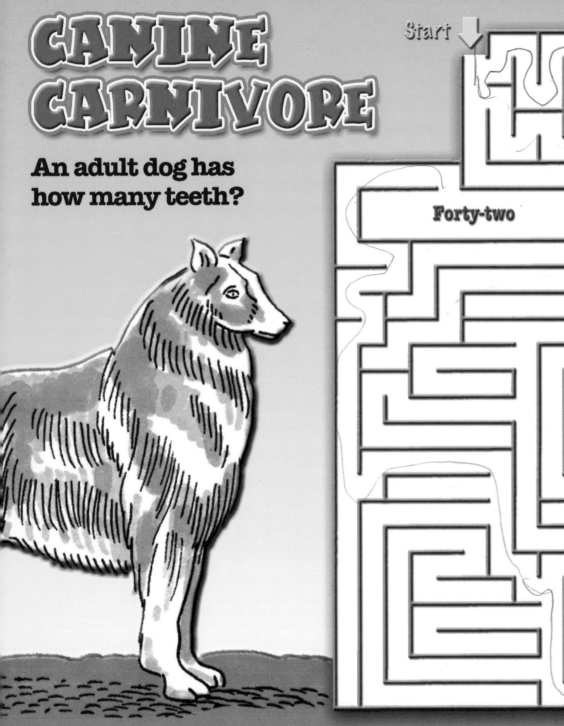

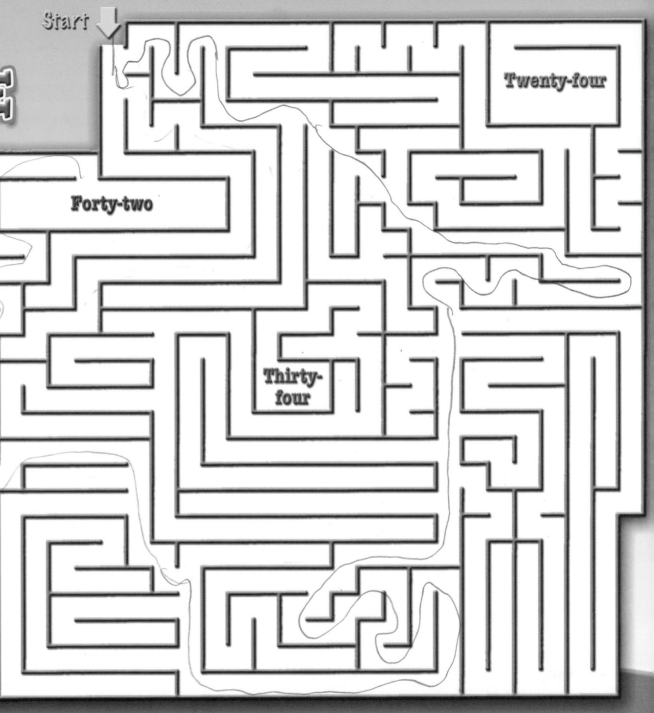

Start

Twenty-four

Forty-two

Thirty-four

WATER LOVER

What does the word *hippopotamus* mean?

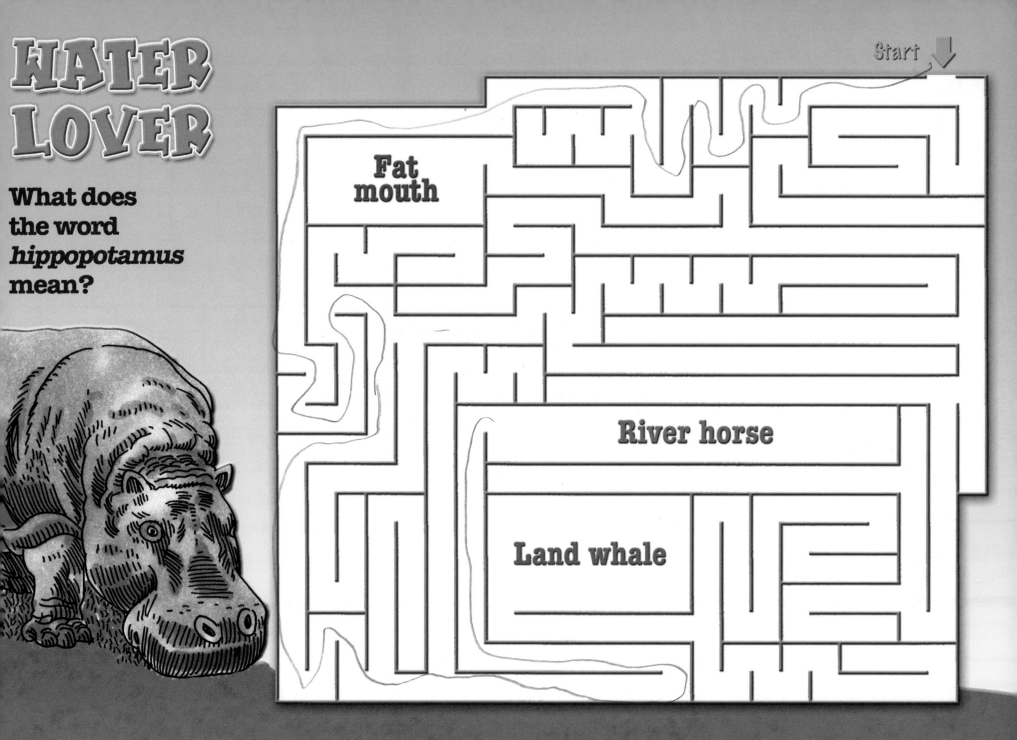

Fat mouth

River horse

Land whale

Start ↓

WILDERNESS WARRIOR

In 1778, Daniel Boone was captured by the Shawnee. His bravery impressed Chief Blackfish, who adopted him and gave him which tribal name?

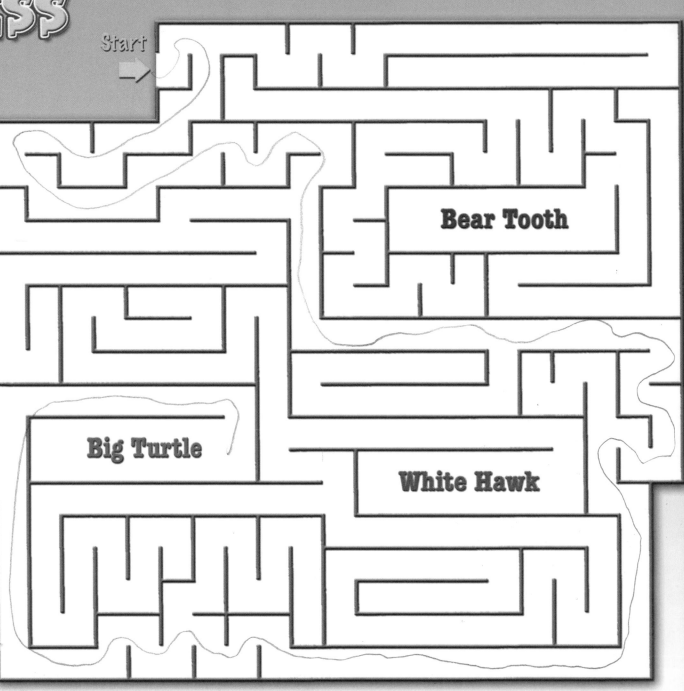

Start

Bear Tooth

Big Turtle

White Hawk

MOTHER OF MODERN NURSING

During which war did Florence Nightingale give medical aid to the troops?

Crimean War

Franco-Prussian War

U.S. Civil War

CHILD'S PLAY

What children's song, still popular today, was composed by Mozart at the age of five?

Start

"The Itsy-Bitsy Spider"

"Ring Around the Rosie"

"Twinkle, Twinkle, Little Star"

HONEYBEES

It takes the nectar from about how many flowers for honeybees to produce one pound of honey?

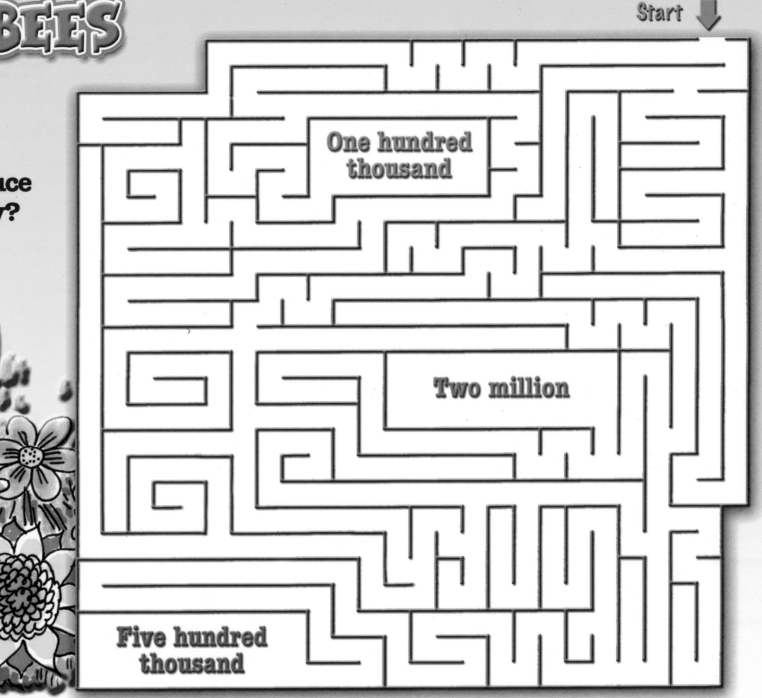

HORSING AROUND

At what age does a filly become a mare?

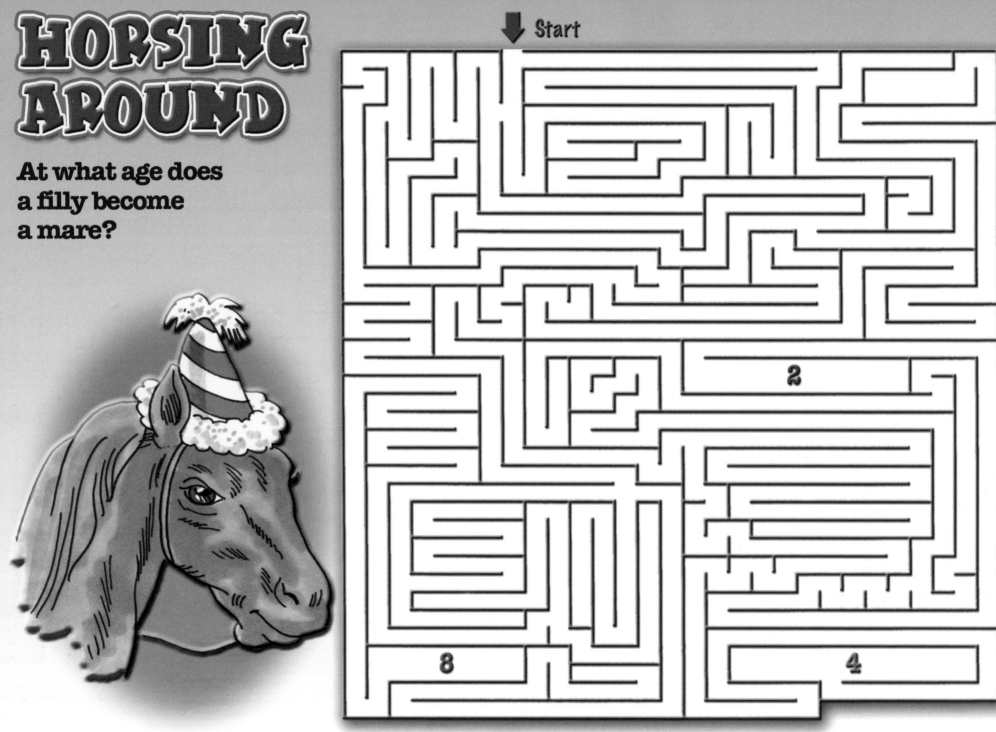

Start

2

8

4

BAND OF GOLD

Finger rings have been found from as far back as 2500 B.C. When did the custom of wearing a golden wedding band become popular?

Ninth century

Sixteenth century

Twentieth century

11

VISIONARY VOYAGER

How many vessels sailed with Christopher Columbus on his second voyage to the New World?

DUFFER'S DELIGHT

What are the odds that a golfer will get a hole in one?

Start

1 in 10,000

1 in 20,000 to 1 in 33,000

1 in 1,000 to 1 in 5,000

14

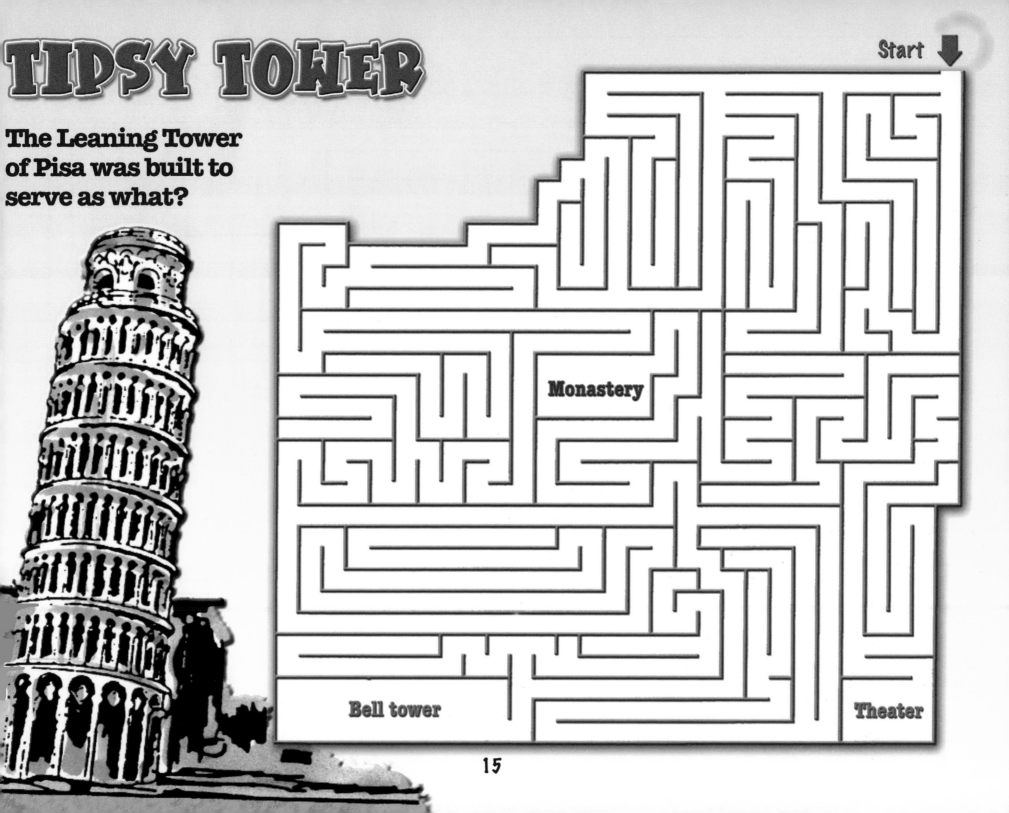

TIPSY TOWER

The Leaning Tower of Pisa was built to serve as what?

Start

Monastery

Bell tower

Theater

MONKEY BUSINESS

What is a group of baboons called?

I HATE CROWDS!

Start

Bunch

Horde

Troop

APPRECIATION DAY

In which year was Mother's Day made a national holiday?

1944

1924

1914

17

COLLEGIATE GAMES

Which is the oldest college sport still played at U.S. colleges?

Start ⬇

Football

Rowing

Lacrosse

I'VE SEEN IT MANY TIMES!

TURF TAMER

When was the first practical lawn mower invented?

Start

1890

1830

1915

POP TUNES

What is the best-selling musical instrument in the world?

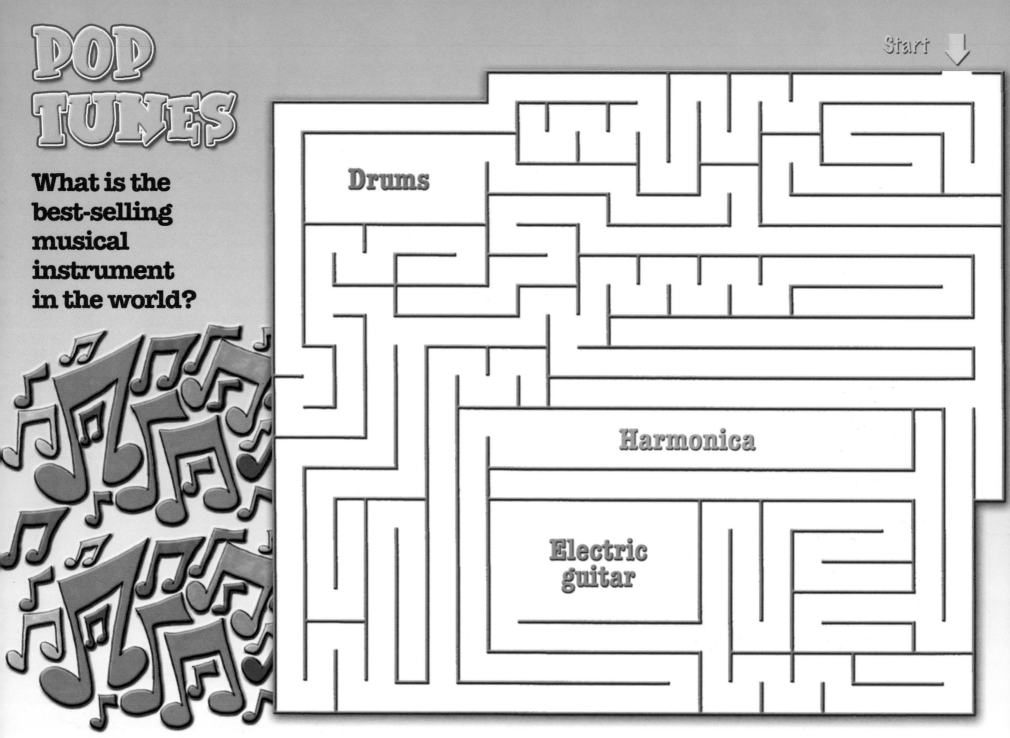

Drums

Harmonica

Electric guitar

RARE GAME

How many batters does a pitcher face in a perfect game (no runs, no hits, no walks)?

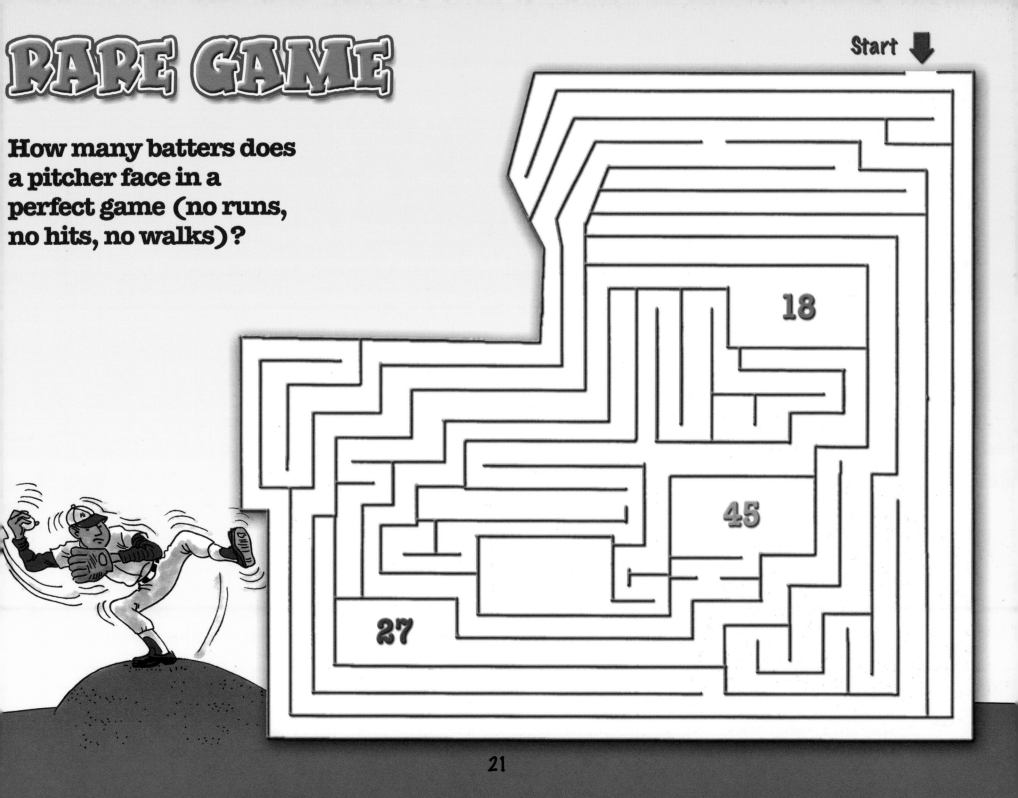

PIONEER SPIRIT

How long did it take Lewis and Clark to reach the Pacific Ocean on their historic trip, which began in St. Louis in 1804?

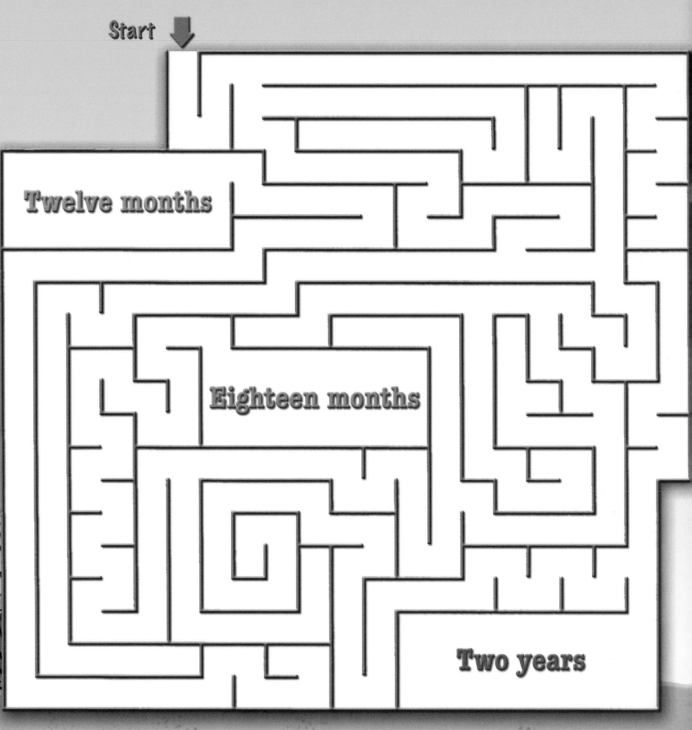

Start

Twelve months

Eighteen months

Two years

WORLD TRAVELER

Who made the famous record-setting, around-the-world trip in 72 days, 6 hours, 11 minutes and 14 seconds in 1889?

IT WASN'T ME.

Start

Nelly Bly

Amelia Earhart

Roald Amundsen

23

ISLAND OF RICHES

Which island is known as Gem Island, because so many valuable gemstones are found there?

Start

Sri Lanka

Madagascar

Cyprus

NON-REGULATION PLAY

In major-league baseball, what happens if a fielder catches a fly ball with his hat instead of his glove?

Start

The batter is out.

The batter takes three bases.

The fielder is ejected from the game.

25

TIGHT SQUEEZE

The 150-pound Pacific giant octopus can squeeze its entire body through an opening no bigger than the width of what?

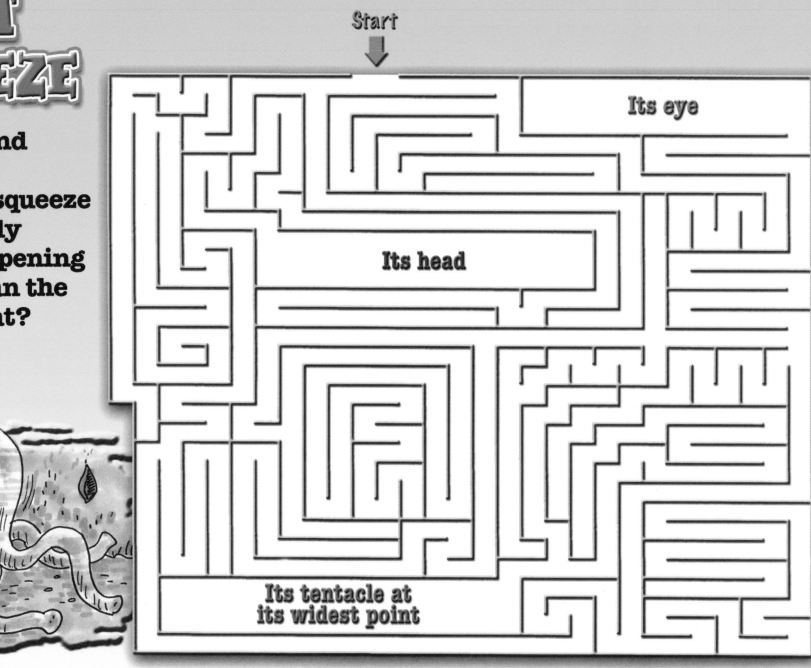

Start

Its eye

Its head

Its tentacle at its widest point

OPTICAL ILLUSION

Each human eye has only one lens. About how many lenses does each dragonfly eye have?

I SEE YOU!

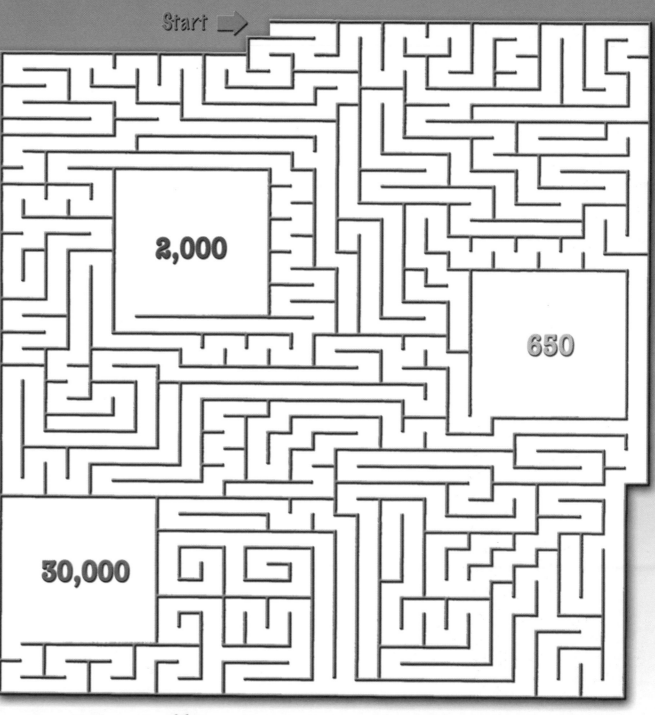

2,000

650

30,000

27

BROTHER BRUINS

How many living species of bears are there?

SILENT BREED

What breed of dog doesn't bark, and cleans its coat with its tongue in the manner of a cat?

Start

Saluki

Basenji

Rhodesian Ridgeback

29

GREEN THUMB

What is a person who studies plants called?

Start

Herbivore

Ecologist

Botanist

HONORABLE MENTION

What is the highest award that a U.S. soldier can receive?

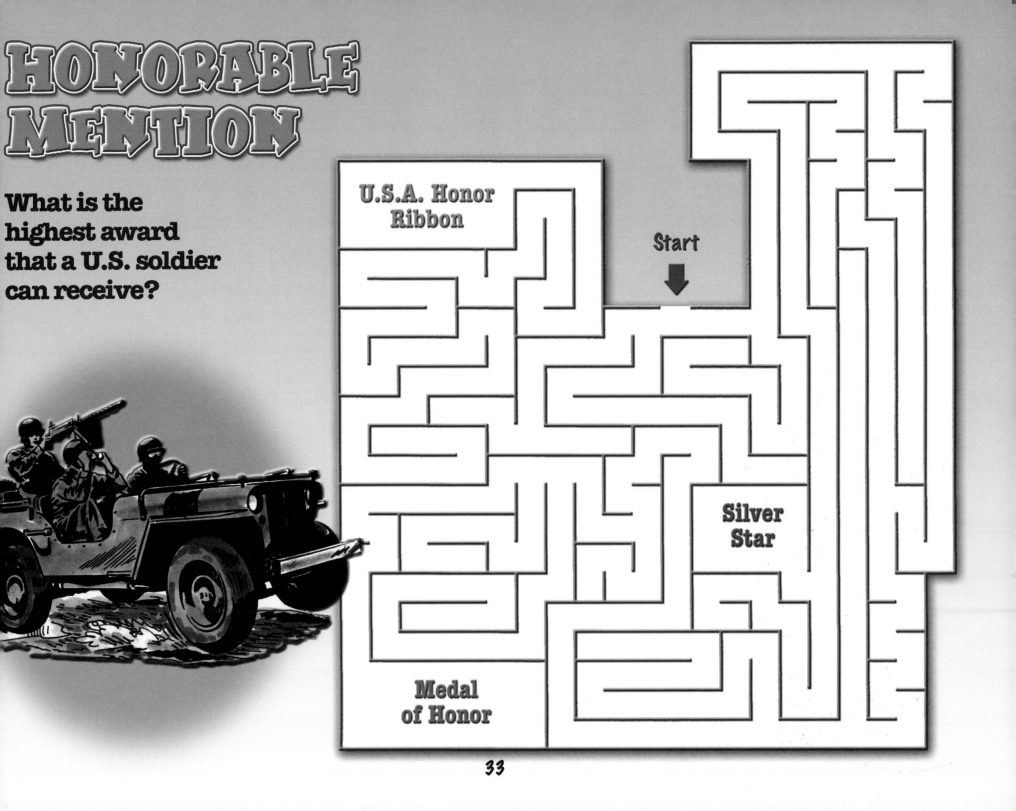

U.S.A. Honor Ribbon

Start

Silver Star

Medal of Honor

PURR-FECT PETS

In ancient Egypt, how did a family mourn when a pet cat died?

They didn't bathe.

They shaved their eyebrows.

They became vegetarians.

TEN-PIN ALLEY

In bowling, what are three strikes in a row called?

Start

Peacock

Turkey

Triangle

35

DOG DAZE

About how many billion hot dogs do Americans consume each year?

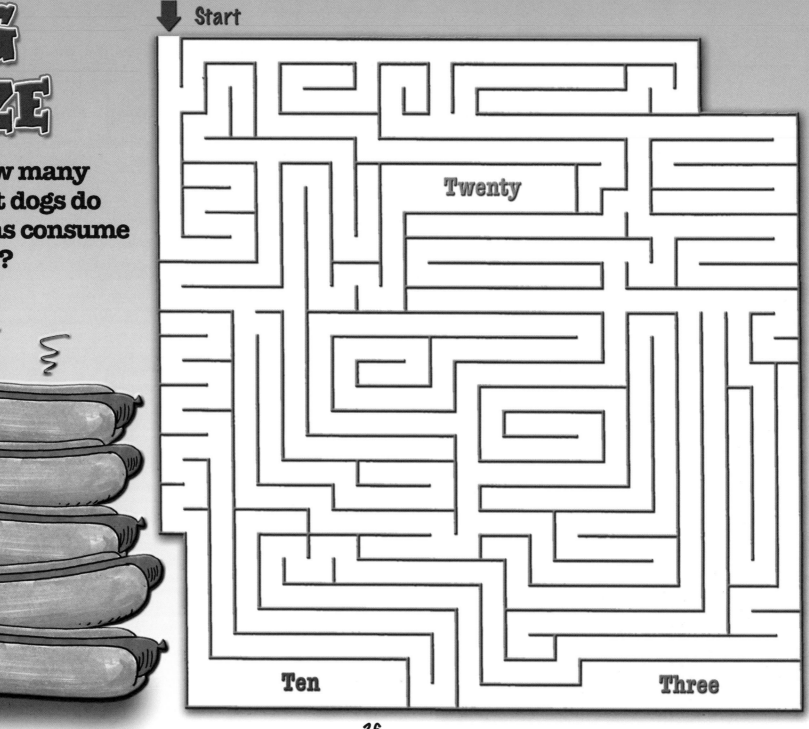

METAMORPHOSIS MASTERS

Start

About how many kinds of butterflies and moths are there?

17 thousand

77 thousand

170 thousand

NORTH VS. SOUTH

Where were the first shots of the Civil War fired?

I'D RATHER BE PLAYING IN A ROCK BAND.

Bull Run

Gettysburg

Fort Sumter

PILGRIM'S PROGRESS

How many days did the Mayflower take to sail from England to America in 1620?

Start ➡

22

44

66

DOCTOR'S ORDERS

During the European plagues of medieval times, what did some doctors recommend to be eaten and also worn around the neck to stay healthy?

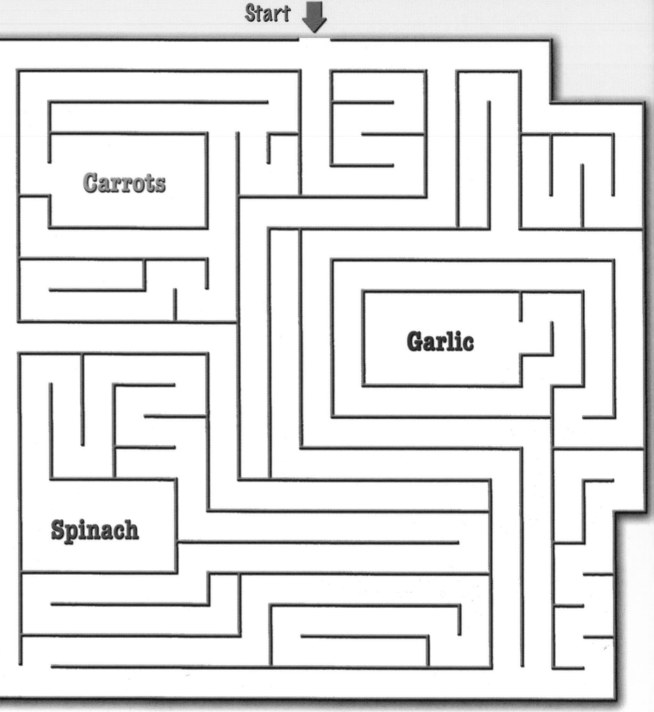

Start

Carrots

Garlic

Spinach

What is it called when a player scores three goals in one game in ice hockey?

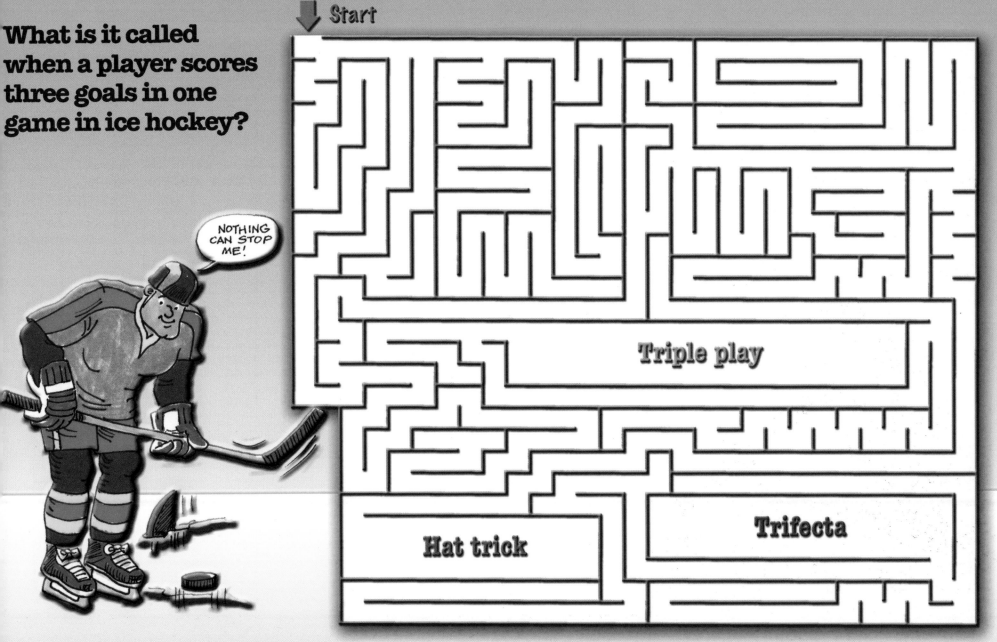

GOING BANANAS

Which country grows the most bananas (about 10 million tons per year)?

AH, NUTS!

How many different uses for the peanut plant did American scientist George Washington Carver come up with?

Start

Three hundred

Seventy-five

One hundred fifty

HOOP DREAMS

How high off the floor are the hoops on a regulation basketball court?

Start

10 feet

12 feet

8 ½ feet

PANDA-MONIUM

About how many pandas are still living in the wild?

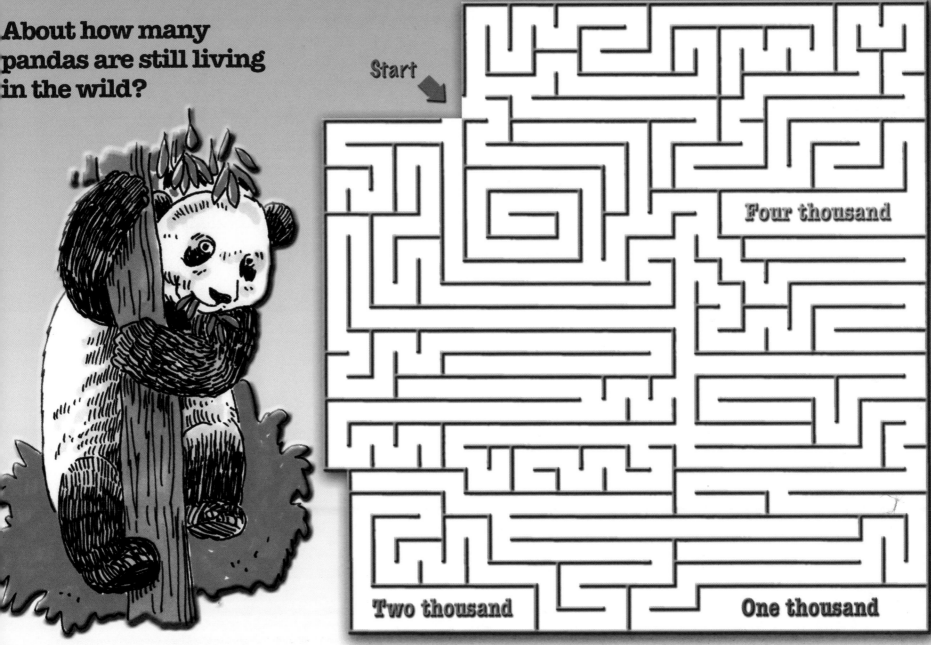

Start

Four thousand

Two thousand

One thousand

CRISIS OF CONSCIENCE

When George Washington was president, what percentage of the U.S. population were slaves?

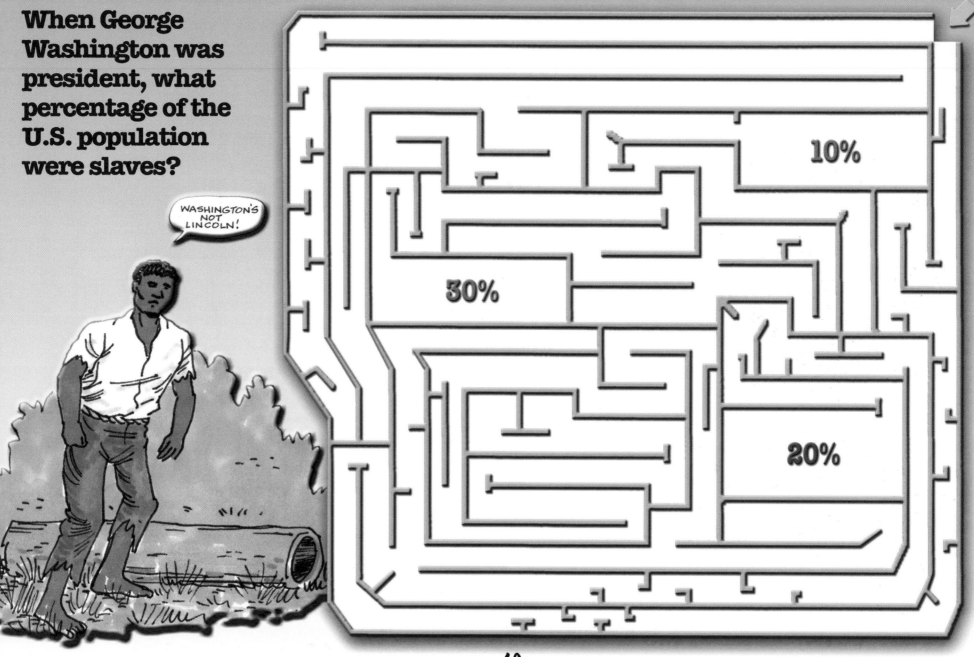

FUZZY FRUIT

What is another name for the kiwifruit?

DELICIOUS!

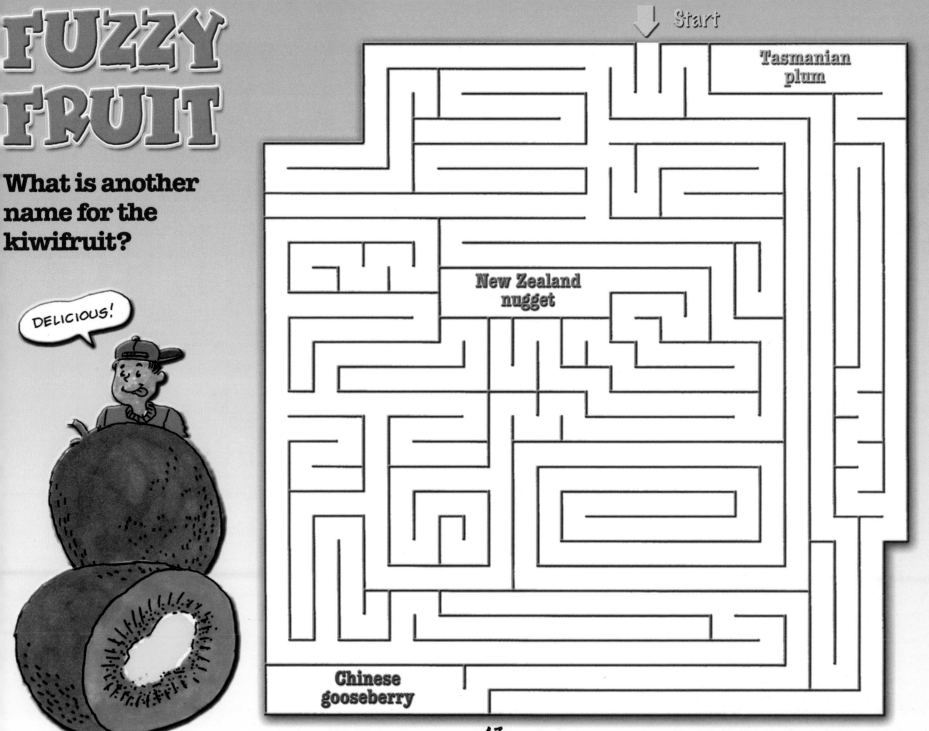

Start

Tasmanian plum

New Zealand nugget

Chinese gooseberry

BUMPER CROP

Which U.S. state produces the most apples?

Start ⬇

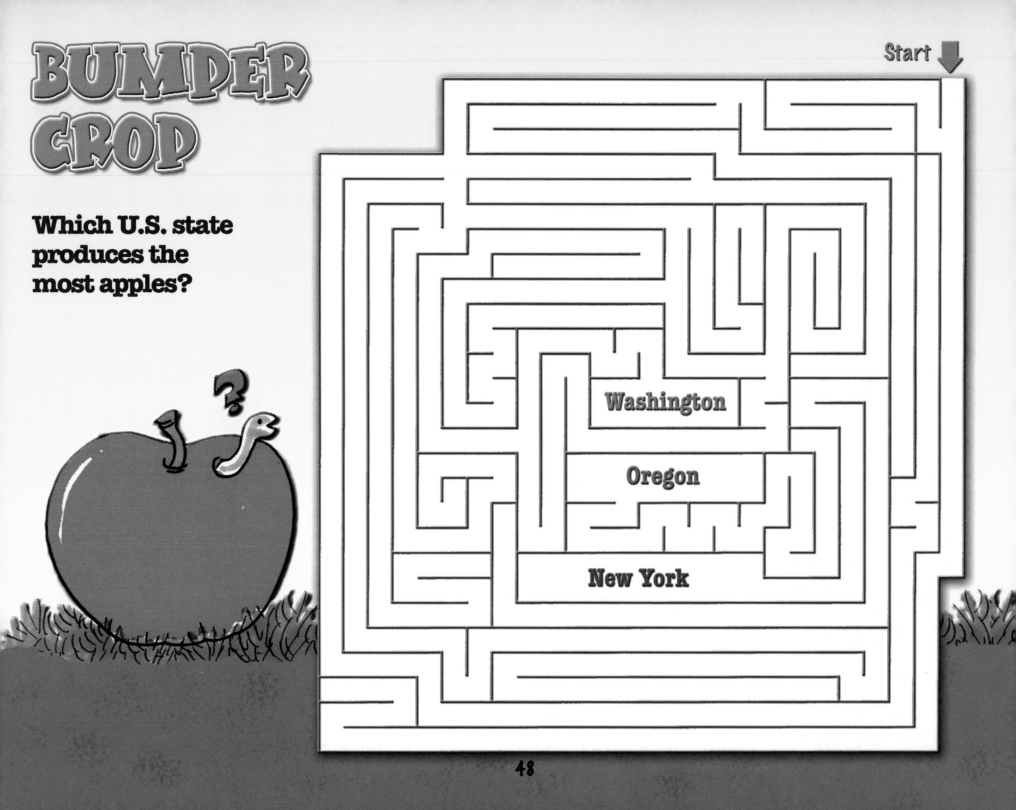

Washington

Oregon

New York

ONE-STOP SHOP

Surgeons in the 17th century performed bloodletting and tooth extraction. What other service did they offer?

Start

Gave haircuts

Sold real estate

Worked in butcher shops

MARKET MASTER

The world's first supermarket opened in the U.S. in 1930. What was it called?

Start

King Kullen

A&P

Publix

DOLLAR DAYS

What is the average life of a one-dollar bill?

Start

Eighteen months

Six months

Four years

LONG-WINDED

In which country did the windmill originate, in about A.D. 644?

Start

Tunisia

The Netherlands

Persia

MAN'S BEST FRIEND

Fido is a common name for a pet dog. It comes from a Latin word meaning what?

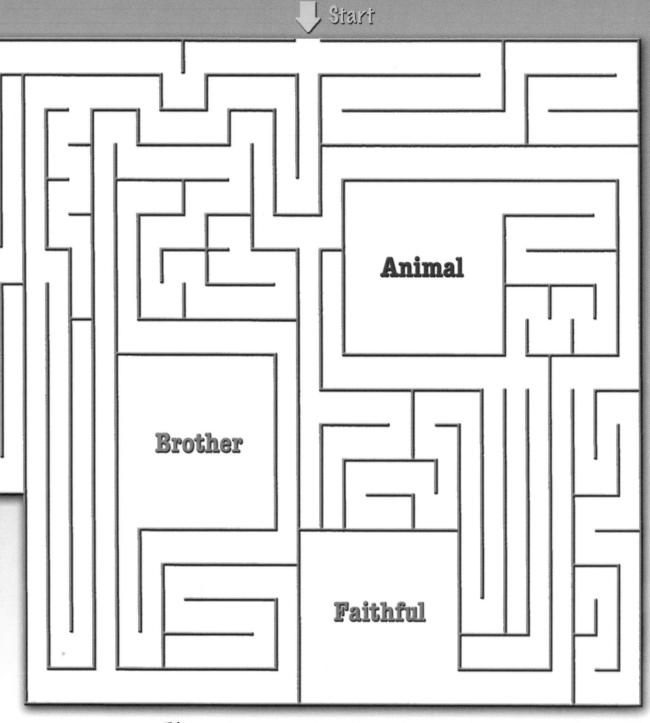

Start

Animal

Brother

Faithful

HANG TIME

About how many Mexican free-tailed bats roost in Texas's Bracken Cave?

NO VACANCY

Start

2 million

10 million

20 million

REVOLUTIONARY HERO

Start ⬇

How old was U.S. naval hero John Paul Jones when he became captain of his own ship?

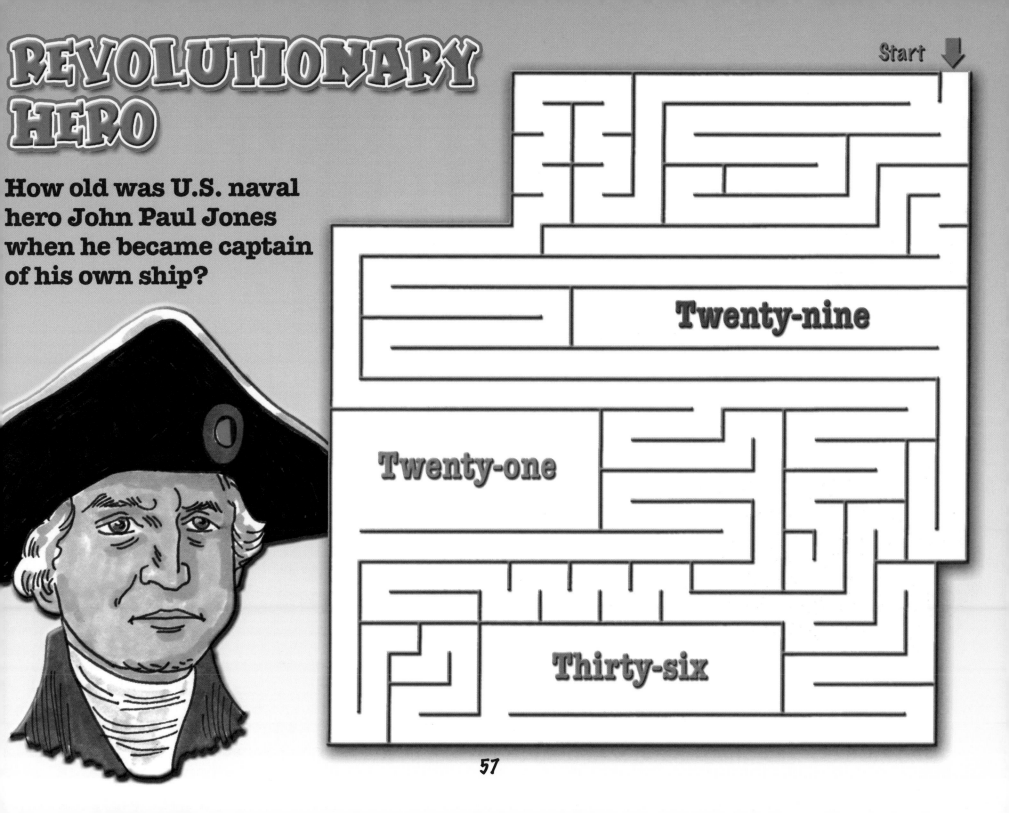

Twenty-nine

Twenty-one

Thirty-six

57

BIG APPLE

New York City holds which of these world records?

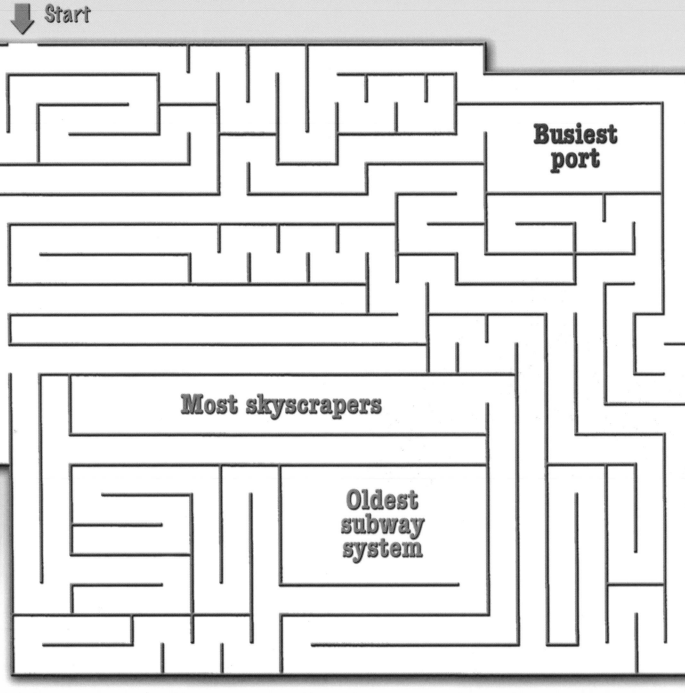

Start

Busiest port

Most skyscrapers

Oldest subway system

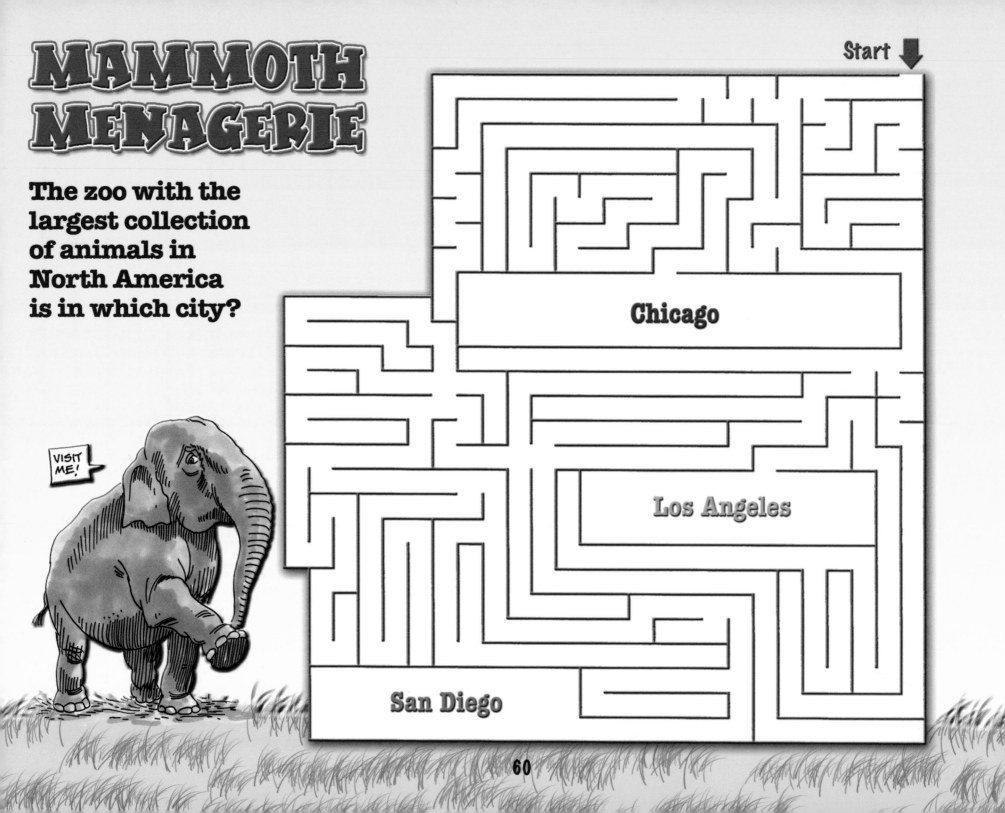

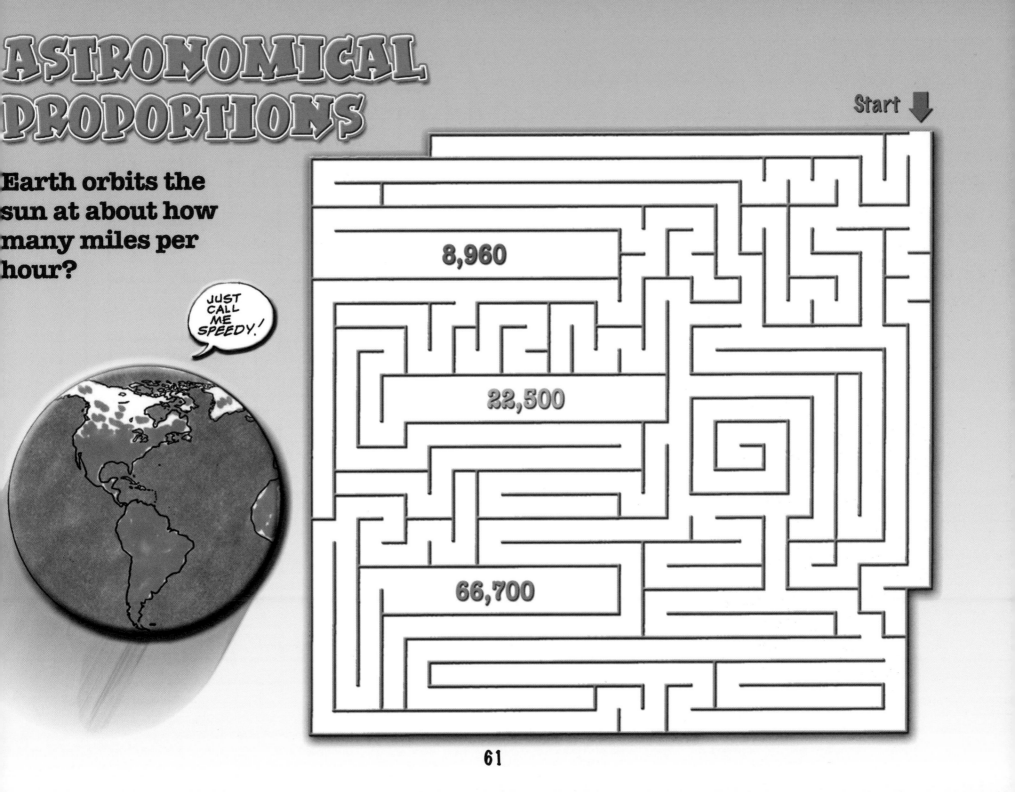

MIGHTY TREE

An oak tree must be at least how many years old before it can produce acorns?

Start

Ten

Fifty

Twenty

SNOW BOWL

How much snow fell in the greatest single snowstorm ever at the Mt. Shasta Ski Bowl, California, February 13-19, 1959?

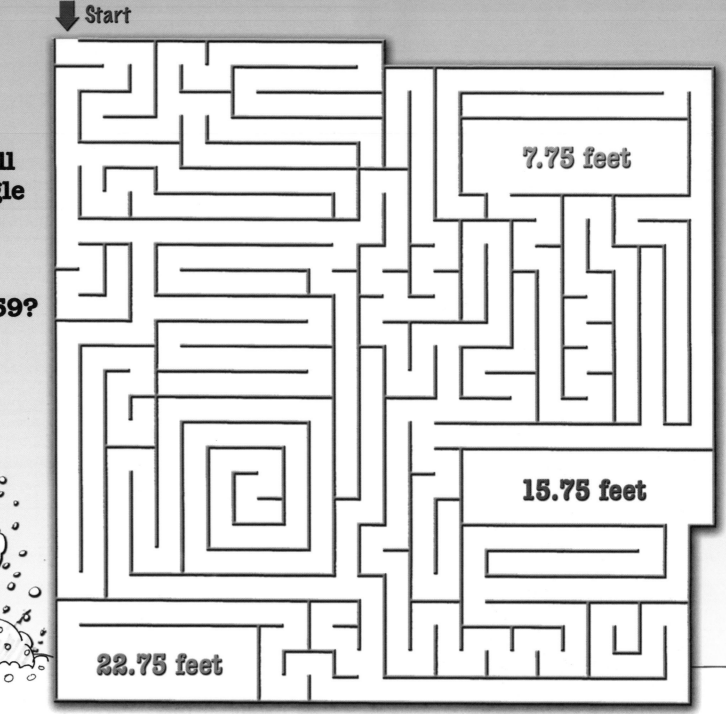

Start

7.75 feet

15.75 feet

22.75 feet

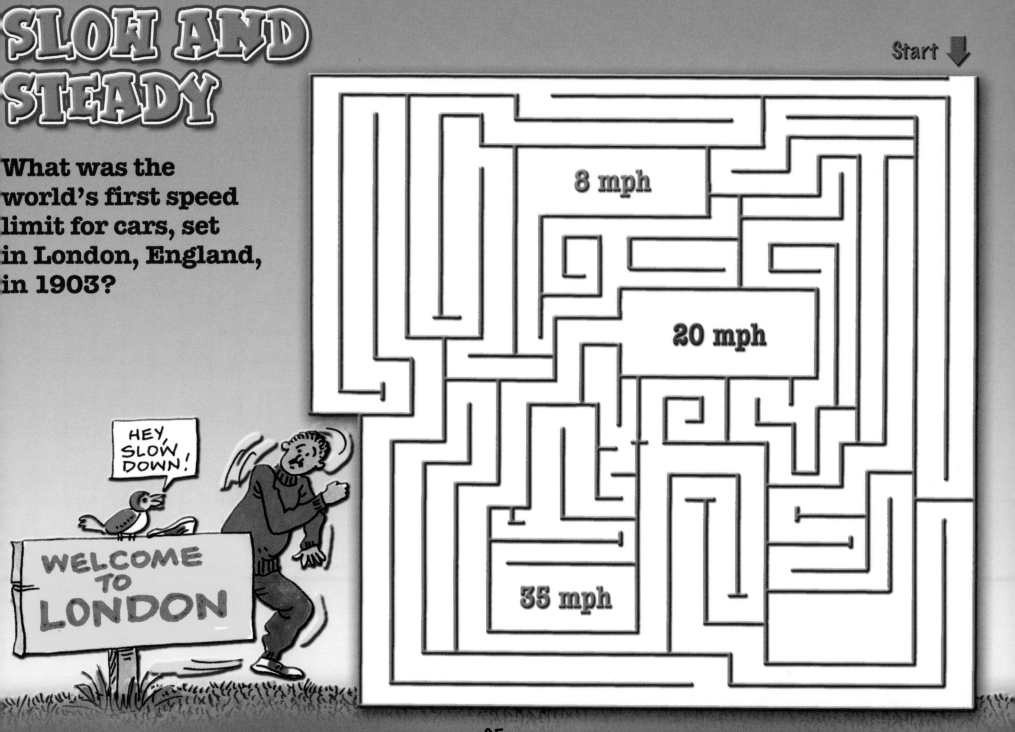

SLOW AND STEADY

WATCH THE BIRDIE!

In Olympic badminton, the birdie, or shuttlecock, must have how many feathers?

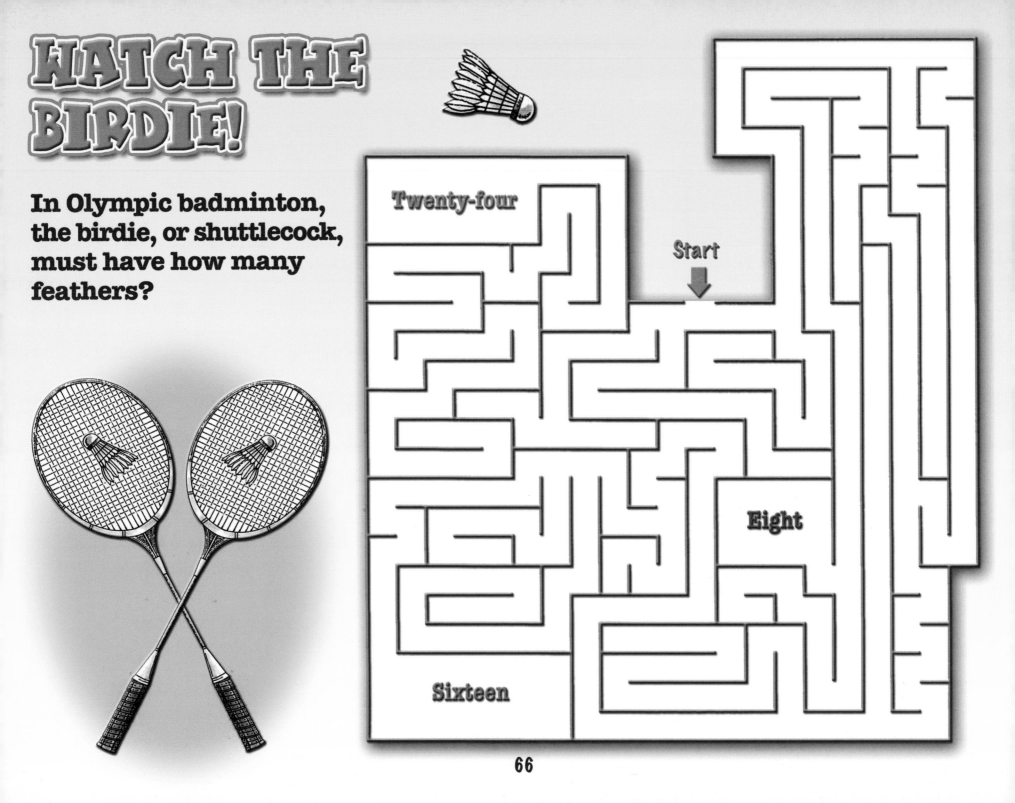

Twenty-four

Start

Eight

Sixteen

FREEDOM FIGHTERS

During the Civil War, about how many African Americans served in the Union Army?

Fifty thousand

Two hundred thousand

Four thousand

Start

RAPTOR REVIVAL

In 1986, there were only fifteen living California condors. Due to conservation efforts, about how many are there today?

Start

Fifty

Six hundred

Three hundred

SIBLING RIVALRY

According to legend, which city did Romulus and Remus found in the 8th century B.C.?

Start

Athens

Baghdad

Rome

COURAGEOUS GUIDE

Who was a "conductor" on the Underground Railroad?

Frederick Douglass

Sojourner Truth

Harriet Tubman

FERTILE GROUND

Which continent has the greatest variety of plants and animals?

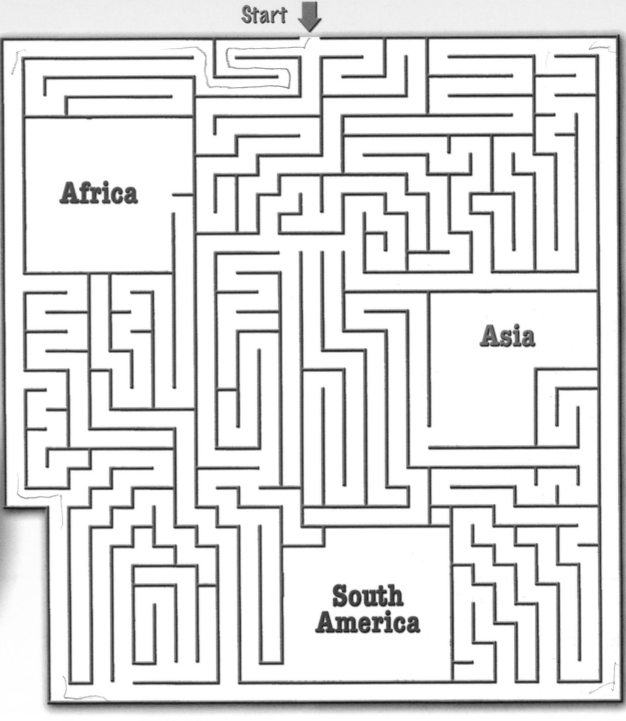

Start

Africa

Asia

South America

YEE-HA

When was the first Kentucky Derby?

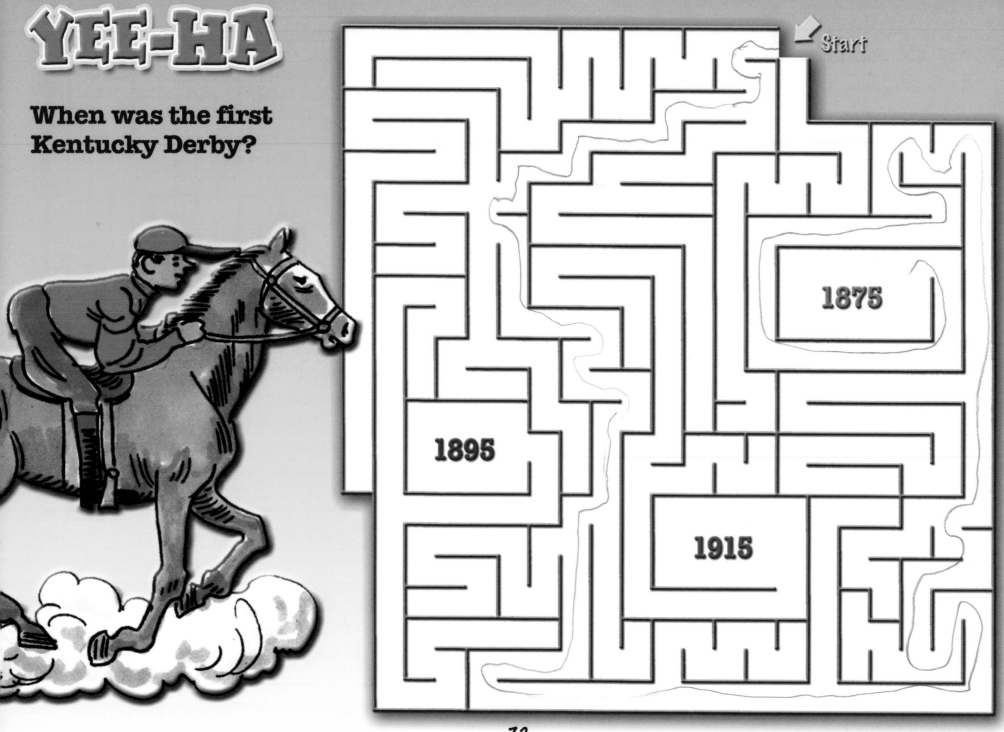

Start

1875

1895

1915

LIQUID ICE

One inch of rain equals how many inches of snow, in water content?

FACE TIME

If the average man never shaved or trimmed his beard, about how long would it grow in his lifetime?

Start

Thirty feet

Twenty feet

Ten feet

PAY DAY

When the first U.S. Minimum Wage Law was passed in 1938, how much was the minimum wage?

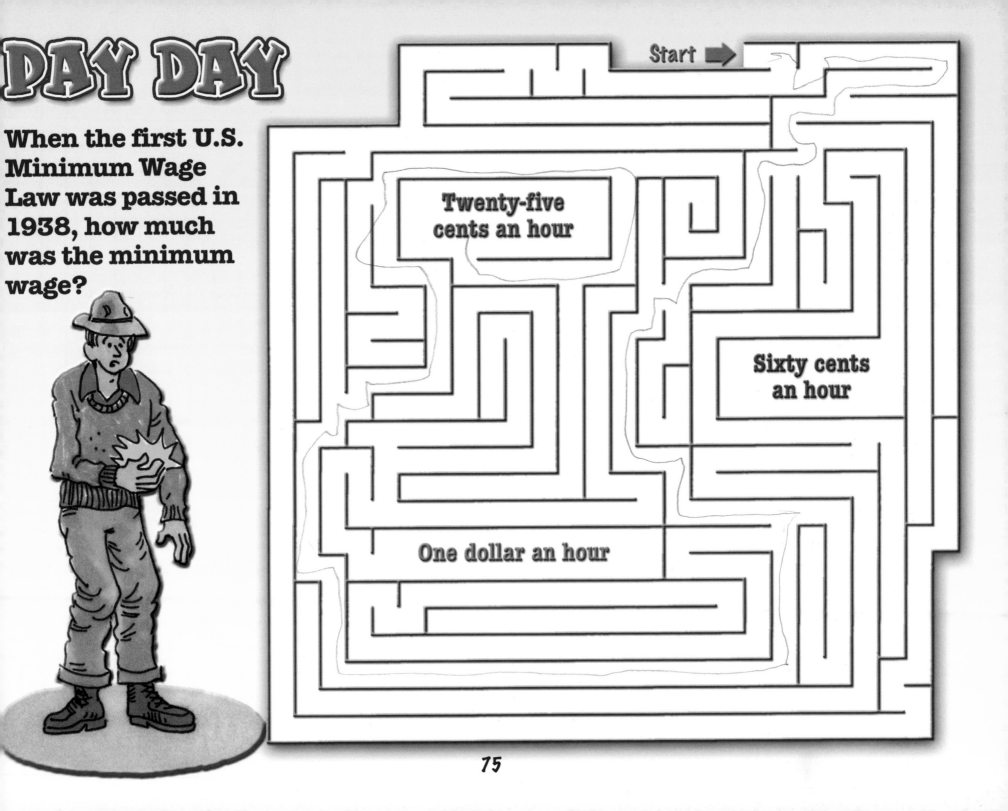

Start ➡

Twenty-five cents an hour

Sixty cents an hour

One dollar an hour

OLD SPORT

Which of these sports was once part of the Olympic Games?

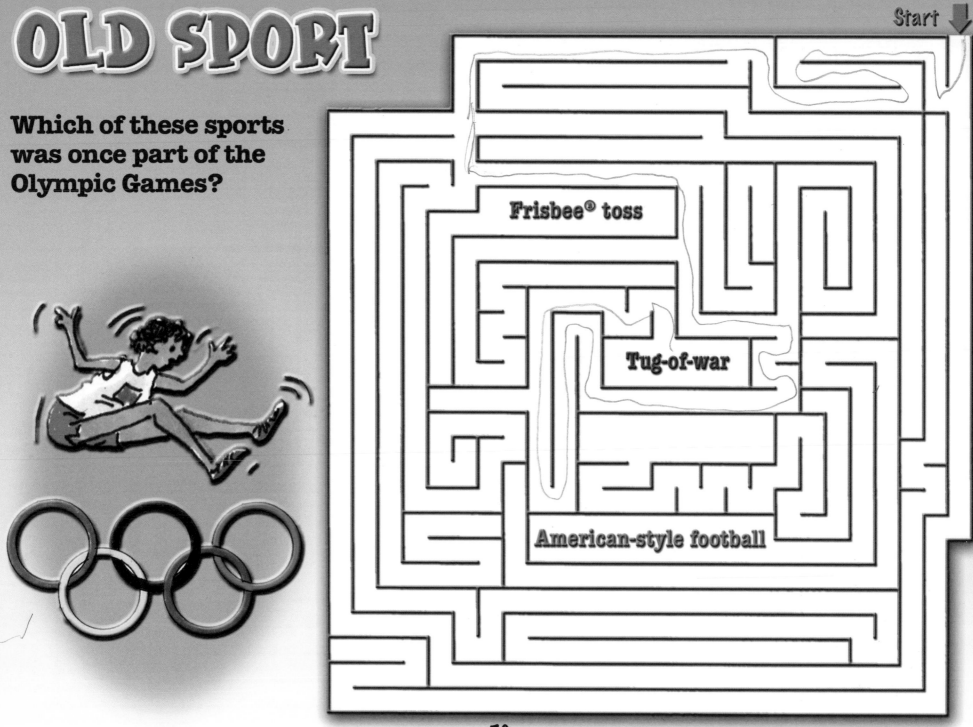

Frisbee® toss

Tug-of-war

American-style football

HANGING OUT

A young orangutan will stay with its mother until it is how many years old?

STAY WITH MAMA, BABY.

NATURE'S PRESERVATIVE

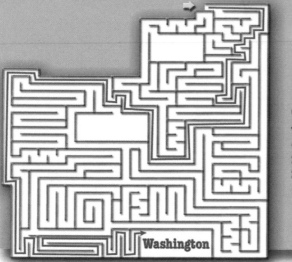

Washington

TRIVIA TIDBIT!

The petrified wood was created from centuries of lava flows from volcanic fissures.

A STICKY SITUATION

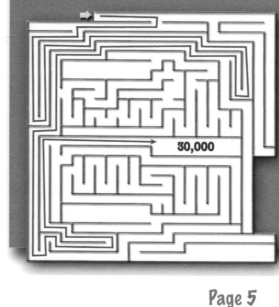

30,000

TRIVIA TIDBIT!

Over 2 billion pounds of peanuts are grown in the U.S. every year; approximately half that amount is eaten as peanut butter.

CANINE CARNIVORE

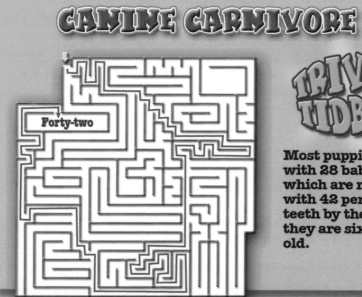

Forty-two

TRIVIA TIDBIT!

Most puppies start with 28 baby teeth, which are replaced with 42 permanent teeth by the time they are six months old.

WATER LOVER

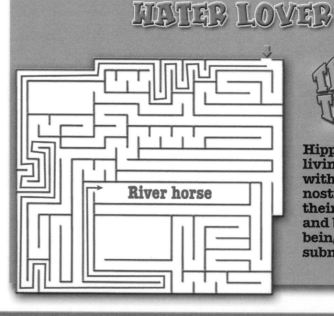

River horse

TRIVIA TIDBIT!

Hippos are built for living in water, with their eyes and nostrils high on their head to see and breathe while being mostly submerged.

WILDERNESS WARRIOR

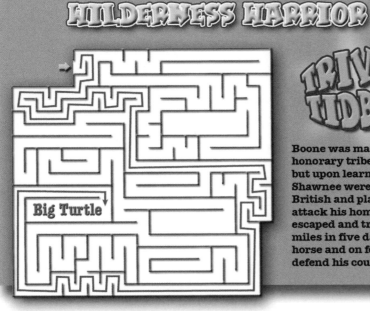

Big Turtle

TRIVIA TIDBIT!

Boone was made an honorary tribe member, but upon learning that the Shawnee were helping the British and planning to attack his hometown, he escaped and traveled 160 miles in five days, by horse and on foot, to defend his country.

MOTHER OF MODERN NURSING

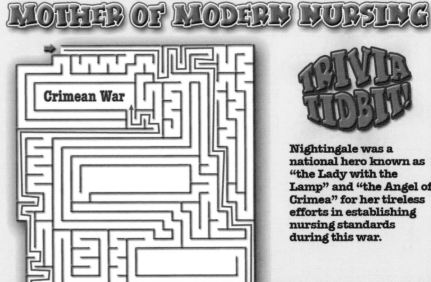

Crimean War

TRIVIA TIDBIT!

Nightingale was a national hero known as "the Lady with the Lamp" and "the Angel of Crimea" for her tireless efforts in establishing nursing standards during this war.

CHILD'S PLAY

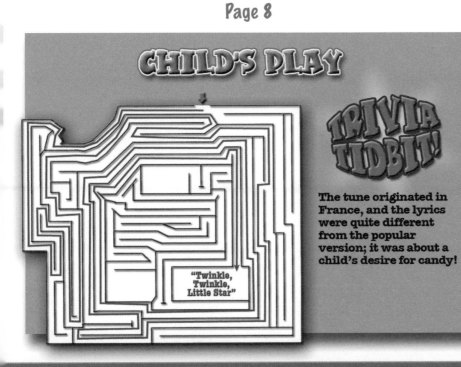

"Twinkle, Twinkle, Little Star"

TRIVIA TIDBIT!

The tune originated in France, and the lyrics were quite different from the popular version; it was about a child's desire for candy!

HONEYBEES

Two million

TRIVIA TIDBIT!

Honeybees are excellent cross-pollinators because they fly between plants of the same species in any given trip.

HORSING AROUND

TRIVIA TIDBIT!

Mares, like most horses, have a basic instinct to form friendship bonds within a herd or group.

BAND OF GOLD

TRIVIA TIDBIT!

In many Western cultures, wedding bands are worn on the fourth finger of the left hand, which contains a vein that leads directly to the heart.

Sixteenth century

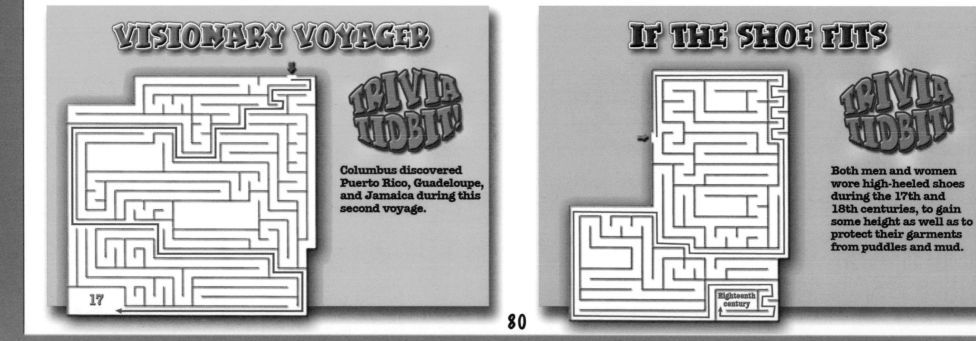

VISIONARY VOYAGER

TRIVIA TIDBIT!

Columbus discovered Puerto Rico, Guadeloupe, and Jamaica during this second voyage.

IF THE SHOE FITS

TRIVIA TIDBIT!

Both men and women wore high-heeled shoes during the 17th and 18th centuries, to gain some height as well as to protect their garments from puddles and mud.

Eighteenth century

Page 14

DUFFER'S DELIGHT

1 in 20,000 to 1 in 33,000

TRIVIA TIDBIT!

Mark Twain described the game of golf as "a good walk spoiled."

Page 15

TIPSY TOWER

Bell tower

TRIVIA TIDBIT!

Galileo performed his famous experiments with gravity and falling objects from the top of the tower.

Page 16

MONKEY BUSINESS

Troop

TRIVIA TIDBIT!

A troop population can consist of as few as 30 members, to over 100 members.

Page 17

APPRECIATION DAY

1914

TRIVIA TIDBIT!

Mother's Day began as a proclamation by Julia Ward Howe in 1870 for a day of observance to promote peace.

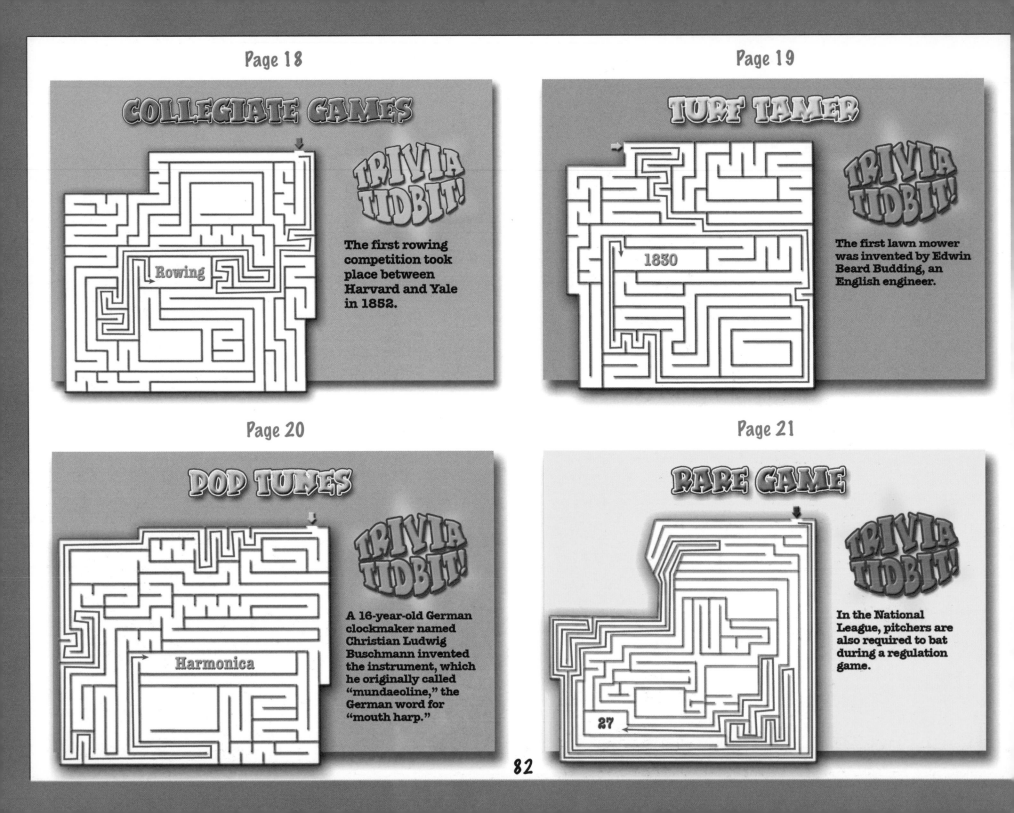

Page 18

COLLEGIATE GAMES

Rowing

TRIVIA TIDBIT!

The first rowing competition took place between Harvard and Yale in 1852.

Page 19

TURF TAMER

1830

TRIVIA TIDBIT!

The first lawn mower was invented by Edwin Beard Budding, an English engineer.

Page 20

POP TUNES

Harmonica

TRIVIA TIDBIT!

A 16-year-old German clockmaker named Christian Ludwig Buschmann invented the instrument, which he originally called "mundaeoline," the German word for "mouth harp."

Page 21

RARE GAME

27

TRIVIA TIDBIT!

In the National League, pitchers are also required to bat during a regulation game.

PIONEER SPIRIT

Eighteen months

Meriwether Lewis and William Clark were originally sent by President Jefferson to find a waterway between the Atlantic and Pacific Oceans, which they ultimately did not find. The expedition did discover significant information, however, about western United States civilization for future settlement.

WORLD TRAVELER

Nelly Bly

Nelly Bly (pseudonym of Elizabeth Cochrane Seaman) traveled by steamship and train in an attempt to beat the travel time of the fictional journey described in Jules Verne's novel, *Around the World in 80 Days*.

ISLAND OF RICHES

Sri Lanka

A leading exporter of gemstones, Sri Lanka was known as Ceylon until 1972, when a new constitution was instituted.

NON-REGULATION PLAY

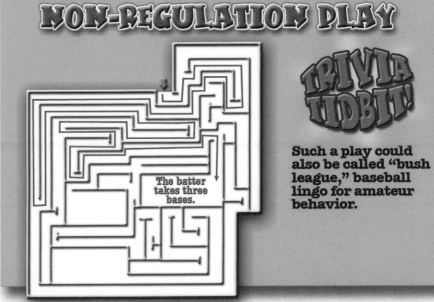

The batter takes three bases.

Such a play could also be called "bush league," baseball lingo for amateur behavior.

TIGHT SQUEEZE

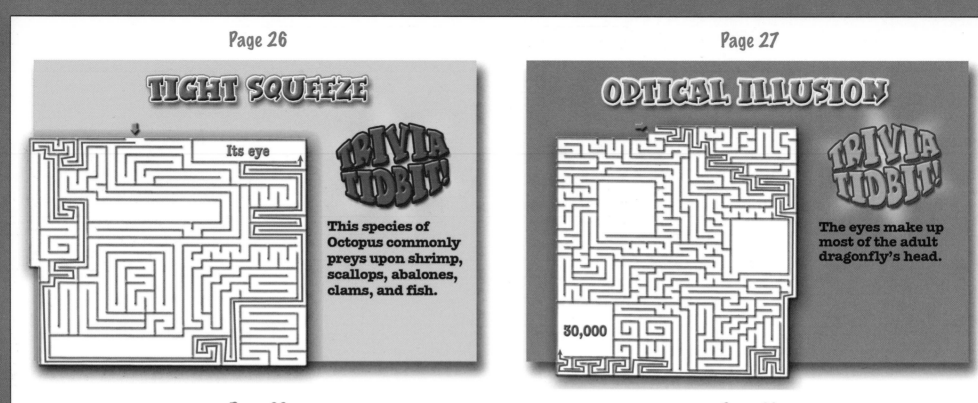

Its eye

TRIVIA TIDBIT!

This species of Octopus commonly preys upon shrimp, scallops, abalones, clams, and fish.

OPTICAL ILLUSION

30,000

TRIVIA TIDBIT!

The eyes make up most of the adult dragonfly's head.

BROTHER BRUINS

Eight

TRIVIA TIDBIT!

The eight species are the Giant Panda, the Spectacled Bear, the Sun Bear, the Sloth Bear, the Asiatic Black Bear, the Black Bear, the Brown Bear, and the Polar Bear.

SILENT BREED

Basenji

TRIVIA TIDBIT!

The Basenji is also called the Congo Bush Dog or Belgian Congo Dog.

SEA CAMEL

BIG CHEESE

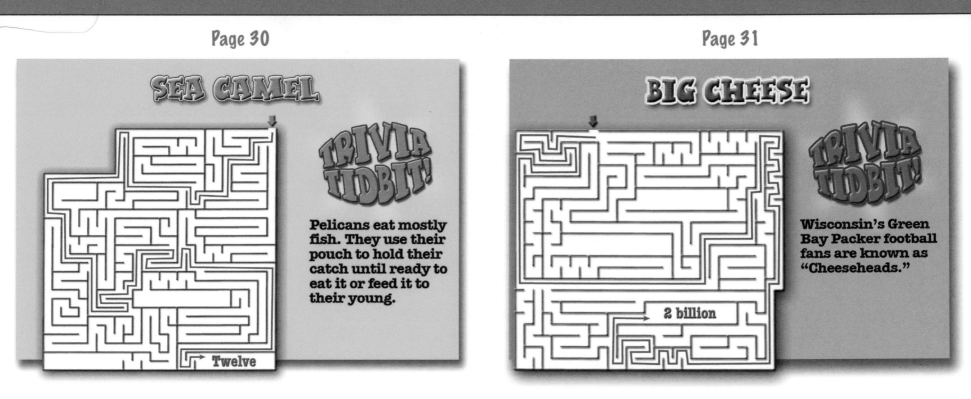

→ Twelve

TRIVIA TIDBIT!

Pelicans eat mostly fish. They use their pouch to hold their catch until ready to eat it or feed it to their young.

→ 2 billion

TRIVIA TIDBIT!

Wisconsin's Green Bay Packer football fans are known as "Cheeseheads."

GREEN THUMB

↓ Botanist

TRIVIA TIDBIT!

An ecologist studies the environment; a herbivore is an animal that eats only plants.

HONORABLE MENTION

↓ Medal of Honor

TRIVIA TIDBIT!

The medal is awarded to those who have risked their lives above and beyond the call of duty.

PURR-FECT PETS

TRIVIA TIDBIT!

Cats were revered by the ancient Egyptians; they were often depicted in tomb paintings that described family life.

They became vegetarians.

TEN-PIN ALLEY

TRIVIA TIDBIT!

Turkey

A score of 300 is a perfect game (and a rare event).

DOG DAZE

TRIVIA TIDBIT!

Twenty

Americans will eat 150 million hot dogs on Independence Day—enough to cover the distance between Washington, D.C., and Los Angeles, California, over 5 times.

METAMORPHOSIS MASTERS

TRIVIA TIDBIT!

Butterflies and moths are cultivated for their silk production.

170 thousand

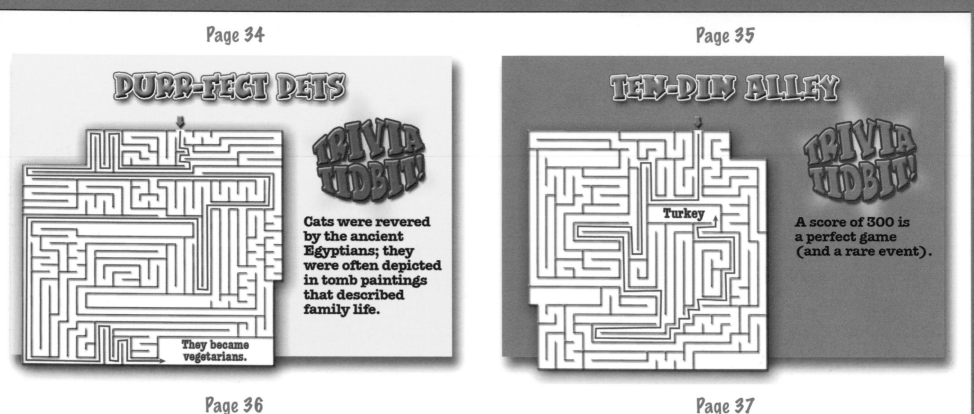

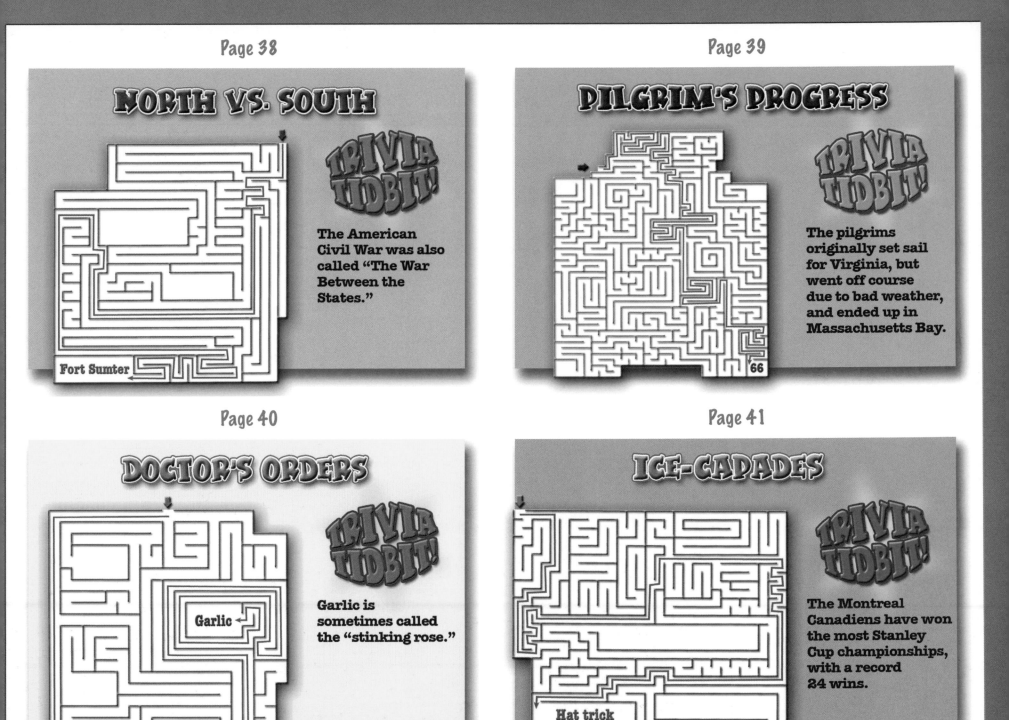

NORTH VS. SOUTH

TRIVIA TIDBIT!

The American Civil War was also called "The War Between the States."

Fort Sumter

PILGRIM'S PROGRESS

TRIVIA TIDBIT!

The pilgrims originally set sail for Virginia, but went off course due to bad weather, and ended up in Massachusetts Bay.

66

DOCTOR'S ORDERS

TRIVIA TIDBIT!

Garlic is sometimes called the "stinking rose."

Garlic

ICE-CAPADES

TRIVIA TIDBIT!

The Montreal Canadiens have won the most Stanley Cup championships, with a record 24 wins.

Hat trick

GOING BANANAS

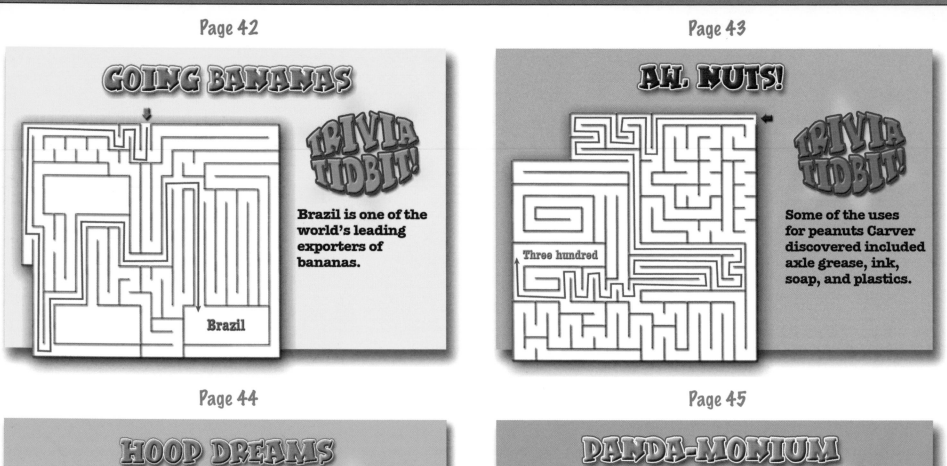

TRIVIA TIDBIT!

Brazil is one of the world's leading exporters of bananas.

Brazil

AW, NUTS!

Three hundred

TRIVIA TIDBIT!

Some of the uses for peanuts Carver discovered included axle grease, ink, soap, and plastics.

HOOP DREAMS

10 feet

TRIVIA TIDBIT!

Dr. James Naismith invented basketball in 1861. The first games were played using a soccer ball and two peach baskets for goals.

PANDA-MONIUM

TRIVIA TIDBIT!

The giant panda's diet consists mainly of bamboo.

One thousand

CRISIS OF CONSCIENCE

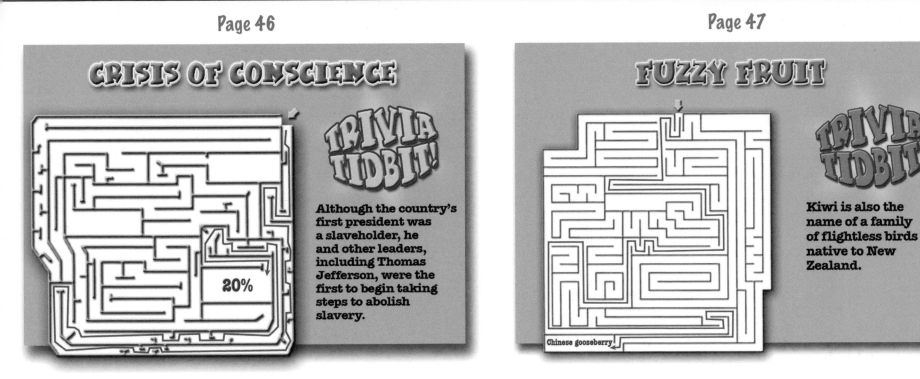

TRIVIA TIDBIT!

Although the country's first president was a slaveholder, he and other leaders, including Thomas Jefferson, were the first to begin taking steps to abolish slavery.

20%

FUZZY FRUIT

TRIVIA TIDBIT!

Kiwi is also the name of a family of flightless birds native to New Zealand.

Chinese gooseberry

BUMPER CROP

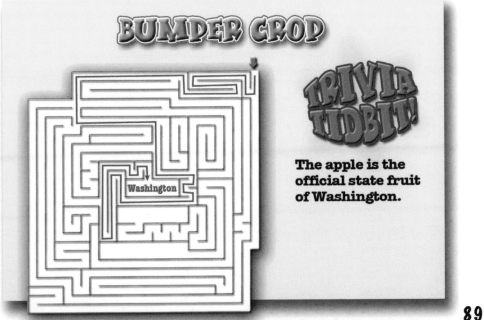

TRIVIA TIDBIT!

The apple is the official state fruit of Washington.

Washington

WINDOWS ON THE WORLD

TRIVIA TIDBIT!

On a clear day, you can see sights as distant as 80 miles from the top of the Empire State Building, including Pennsylvania, New Jersey, Connecticut, and Massachusetts.

6,500

ONE-STOP SHOP

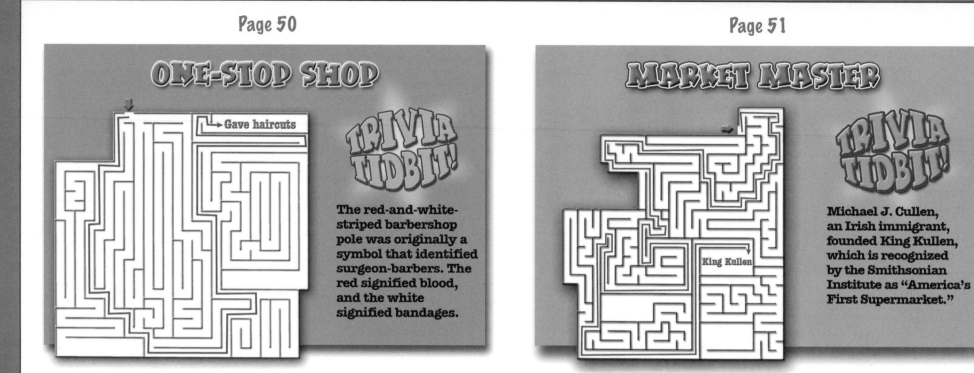

→ Gave haircuts

TRIVIA TIDBIT!

The red-and-white-striped barbershop pole was originally a symbol that identified surgeon-barbers. The red signified blood, and the white signified bandages.

MARKET MASTER

King Kullen

TRIVIA TIDBIT!

Michael J. Cullen, an Irish immigrant, founded King Kullen, which is recognized by the Smithsonian Institute as "America's First Supermarket."

DOLLAR DAYS

→ Eighteen months

TRIVIA TIDBIT!

If you tried to tear a currency note by folding it continuously, it would take 4,000 double-folds (forwards and backwards) before the note would tear.

LONG-WINDED

Persia ←

TRIVIA TIDBIT!

The first windmills, used to generate energy from wind power, were actually designed to rotate horizontally on a vertical shaft.

MAN'S BEST FRIEND

TRIVIA TIDBIT!

Dogs have lived with humans for 14,000 years.

Faithful

PROLIFIC PENGUINS

TRIVIA TIDBIT!

The largest population of penguins can be found in frigid Antarctica, but some species also live in warmer climates, like the Galapagos Islands.

Seventeen

HANG TIME

TRIVIA TIDBIT!

A colony of free-tailed bats can consume 250 tons of insects in a single night.

20 million

REVOLUTIONARY HERO

TRIVIA TIDBIT!

Jones made the famous declaration, "I have not yet begun to fight," as he defeated a powerful British ship during the American Revolution.

Twenty-one

BIG APPLE

Most skyscrapers

TRIVIA TIDBIT!

When the Empire State Building was completed in 1931, it was then the tallest building in the world.

BUSY BEE

Two thousand

TRIVIA TIDBIT!

A queen bee lives an average of one to three years.

MAMMOTH MENAGERIE

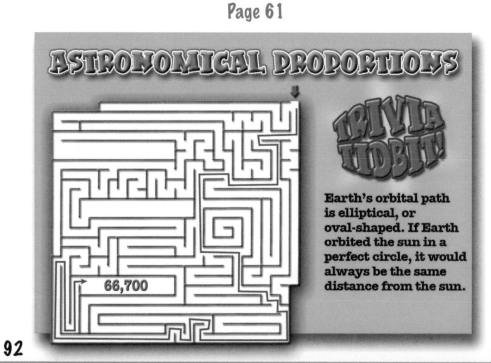

San Diego

TRIVIA TIDBIT!

In 1996, China loaned two giant pandas to the San Diego Zoo in an effort save the species from extinction.

ASTRONOMICAL PROPORTIONS

66,700

TRIVIA TIDBIT!

Earth's orbital path is elliptical, or oval-shaped. If Earth orbited the sun in a perfect circle, it would always be the same distance from the sun.

MIGHTY TREE

TRIVIA TIDBIT!

Oak is a durable wood used to make furniture, cabinetry, and flooring.

Twenty

KICK-OFF TIME

TRIVIA TIDBIT!

The famous college football tournament is traditionally played on New Year's Day in Pasadena, California.

1902

SNOW BOWL

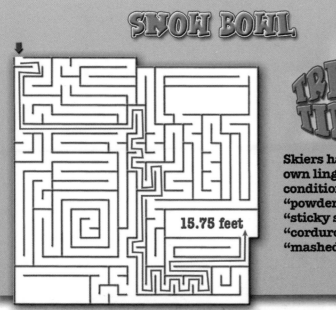

TRIVIA TIDBIT!

Skiers have their own lingo for snow conditions, from "powder snow" and "sticky snow," to "corduroy" and "mashed potatoes"!

15.75 feet

SLOW AND STEADY

TRIVIA TIDBIT!

Prior to that time, the British set the general speed limit at 4 miles per hour.

20 mph

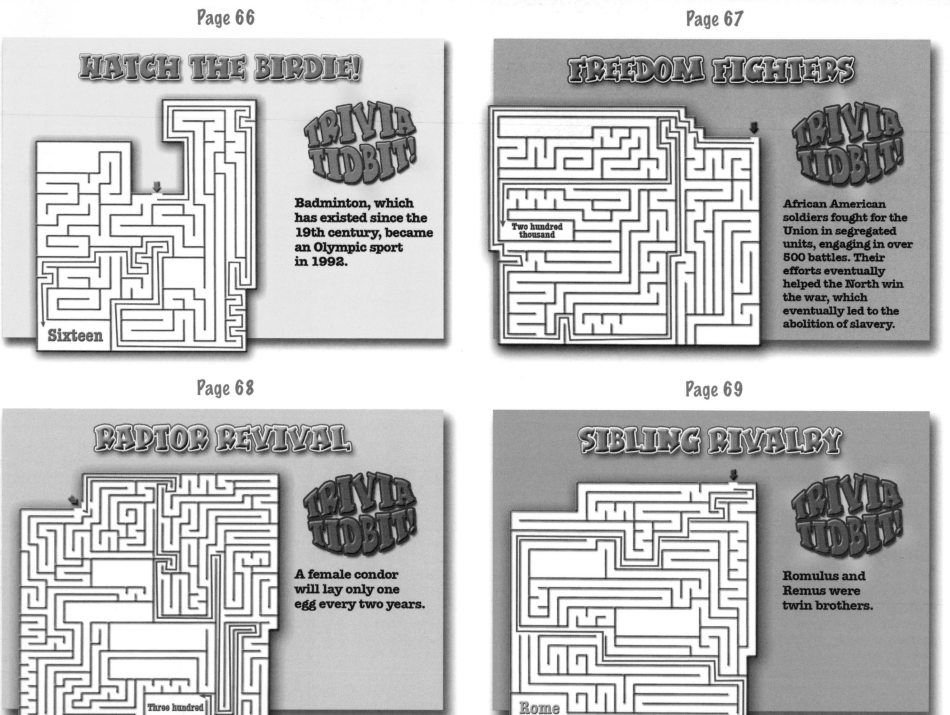

Page 66
WATCH THE BIRDIE!

TRIVIA TIDBIT!

Badminton, which has existed since the 19th century, became an Olympic sport in 1992.

Sixteen

Page 67
FREEDOM FIGHTERS

TRIVIA TIDBIT!

Two hundred thousand

African American soldiers fought for the Union in segregated units, engaging in over 500 battles. Their efforts eventually helped the North win the war, which eventually led to the abolition of slavery.

Page 68
RAPTOR REVIVAL

TRIVIA TIDBIT!

A female condor will lay only one egg every two years.

Three hundred

Page 69
SIBLING RIVALRY

TRIVIA TIDBIT!

Romulus and Remus were twin brothers.

Rome

Page 70

COURAGEOUS GUIDE

TRIVIA TIDBIT!

Tubman helped escort over 300 slaves to freedom over a 10-year period, beginning in 1851.

Harriet Tubman

Page 71

FERTILE GROUND

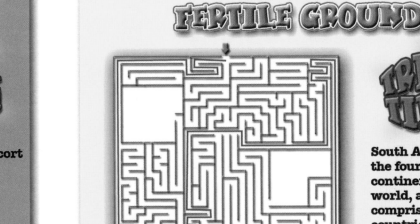

South America

TRIVIA TIDBIT!

South America is the fourth largest continent in the world, and is comprised of 13 countries.

Page 72

YEE-HA

1875

TRIVIA TIDBIT!

The race takes place on the first Saturday in May at Churchill Downs in Louisville, Kentucky. Meriwether Lewis Clark, grandson of explorer William Clark, founded the race and the track.

Page 73

LIQUID ICE

Ten

TRIVIA TIDBIT!

A snowflake is a six-sided ice crystal. No two are alike.

FACE TIME

Thirty feet

TRIVIA TIDBIT!

How fast hair grows depends on its length. Short hair will grow three-quarters of an inch per month, but once hair has reached a foot long, that growth slows by half.

DAY DAY

Twenty-five cents an hour

TRIVIA TIDBIT!

In order for the minimum wage to increase, Congress must pass a bill that the president signs into law.

OLD SPORT

Tug-of-war

TRIVIA TIDBIT!

Other sports no longer played at the Olympic Games include croquet, lacrosse, and water skiing.

HANGING OUT

Six

TRIVIA TIDBIT!

Orangutans can live as long as 60 years, but are considered an endangered species due to increased human destruction of their natural habitats.